READING THE PENINSULA

READING THE PENINSULA

Stories of the Saanich Peninsula

Edited by Sara Dowse

Community Arts Council of the Saanich Peninsula

Community Arts Council of the Saanich Peninsula
Box 2221, Sidney, BC V8L 3S8
www.cacsp.com

Edited by Sara Dowse

Canadian Cataloguing in Publication Data:

READING THE PENINSULA: stories of the Saanich Peninsula

ISBN 0 97334710 4

I.   Canadian literature (English) — fiction and creative non-fiction
II. Title: Reading the Peninsula

Text design by Janice Cook
Cover by Driftwood Designs
Cover painting "Sunrise from Tulista" by Kit McDonald
Printed by A&E Print & Copy Place, Sidney, BC, Canada

Table of Contents

A Place on the Map: Introduction
Sara Dowse

Writers tend to resist being restricted to certain regions, unless they are ones of their own imagining, like William Faulkner's Yoknapatawpha County or Margaret Laurence's town of Manawaka. We like to think our words have universal import and hate to imagine that we're stuck in any one area, and can only speak to readers there. And yet almost every writer I can think of is profoundly imbued with a sense of place. Some readers would put this down to technique: that the ability to evoke particular landscapes is simply part of a writer's stock in trade. I would make a stronger case. Consciously or not, the specific ambience of a particular setting, whether a small rural corner of a continent or a gritty megapolis, informs the way a writer feels and sees, and is often the very wellspring of what he or she writes.

Most of the writers in this volume have lived on the Saanich Peninsula for a while. Some have lived here in the past, and some only come now and then. Whatever the nature of their attachment, this place has got under their skin enough to give them the writer's itch, and make them want to scratch it out on the page.

The idea to produce an anthology of stories set on the peninsula arose in January 2003, in a weaver's studio on the edge of Bazan Bay. It seemed a rather ambitious undertaking, quixotic even, but the idea grew, and soon I was presenting it to the directors of the peninsula's Community Arts Council. New to this sort of thing here, I was doubtful of the reception, to say the least. A preliminary costing showed all too well that I was asking for a substantial commitment. Was there even time to complete such a project within the calendar year? So I put my proposal to them in a lackadaisical fashion, almost certain that it was going to be rejected. "There seem to be a lot of writers here," I began, "and maybe they should get some recognition … "

I shouldn't have been so hard on the directors. They were more than eager to go ahead with the project (though there wasn't a writer among them) and told me to get cracking. The aim was to showcase the talent we have on the peninsula and make every effort to produce the book here, using local typesetting and printing skills as well as those of our writers. It was not to be a commercial publishing venture but perhaps the book would generate enough interest to make a publisher sit up and take notice and eventually take the book on; perhaps this might even be the first book in a long line to come. While it would be largely a collection of prose pieces, the next might be devoted to poetry, or a judicious mixture of both. And so our thoughts ran. We could organise readings around it, to be held like the old ones in a café, or in the public library. Or in the bookshops — Sidney's supposed to be a Booktown, after all. We could launch it at the Sidney Writers Festival. The meeting room at the Emerald Isle was buzzing with our plans.

The writers, too, met the idea with enthusiasm. Through The Writers' Union of Canada and the Federation of BC Writers, we contacted as many in the area as we could find and asked them to spread the word. Even when other commitments kept some from giving us anything, they cheered us on. One writer wrote, "Thanks so much for sending me the information on the book project. I am honoured to be asked but I can't come up with any writing which would qualify. My fiction is set on the west coast of the island and my non-fiction pieces about local boats and boatbuilders hardly qualify as creative. So regrettably it seems that I will have to pass this year but please don't take my name off the list for future editions. "

There were a number of responses in this vein. Given our tight schedule, we had written that we would be happy to accept already published pieces, but not every writer had the right sort of material on hand. But all in all the writers were both positive and generous, and shared the Arts Council's hope that this publication would be a continuing, even annual event.

As for myself, I had another agenda. I came to the peninsula five years ago. After living for forty years in Australia, I was still feeling lost. Try as I might I couldn't quite "get" the landscape. Like a painter coming to this strange new environment who goes on painting red rock and spinifex instead of dark green trees, I was a writer at a loss for words. The closest thing I could find to a gum tree was the gracefully contorted arbutus — "water drinker" as I was eventually to discover through Philip Kevin Paul's poems. As much as my gradual exposure, it was the literature of this coast that was beginning to orient me, deepening my appreciation of the place I'd come to by what had seemed a quirky sequence of accidents.

Nor did I understand much about the community. Here is the opening of an article published in the *Australian Author*:

> I live in a town called Sidney now. Named for the poet, I say, not for the colonial administrator. Sidney with an "i" I say, instead of two "y"s. Or little Sidney instead of big Sydney. I marvel how these places enclose my life, like two bookends propping up the crooked, messy volumes in between.
>
> Sidney is an old sawmill town perched on the tip of the Saanich Peninsula, which juts out, tail-like, from the hind end of Vancouver Island …

And this, another stab at it, but never published:

> The passage from the small island city of Victoria to Vancouver across the Strait of Georgia is a ferry ride of nearly two hours. The British Columbia Ferry is a leviathan of a ship, larger than the largest blue whale, and to a landlubber like me its carrying capacity is impressive. Suspect, actually, in the way that airplanes are to those of us who fly without knowing the first thing about aerodynamics. The ferry lumbers through the water, a perfect white-capped cerulean this time of year. The peaks of the steep Coastal Mountains are dense with snow. Islands thick with cedar float by: large green lozenges luminous as the current in the dappling sun. We pass the horseshoe-shaped Thieves Bay on Pender Island where a man I now know once built a house cantilevered over the cove. He sat on his deck as I do on this vessel, watching eagles soar and glaucous waves mingle and detach themselves below.
>
> Ships have gone down in these waters. At Easter time, in 1911, three schoolmistresses, two of them sisters, took off in the *SS Iroquois* for a holiday on nearby Saltspring Island. The weather was foul, the cargo in the hold shifted,

and the *Iroquois* sank outside Robert's Bay, only a few
blocks from where I now live. The two sisters drowned
but the other schoolmistress was saved when her hair
got tangled on a log that kept her afloat long enough for
an Indian to come to her rescue. (Her students observed
for many years afterward the tenderness in her head and
neck.) Some time later, in October 1947, the *Gulf Stream*,
a ferryboat, hit a rock in a storm just north of Vancouver
and sank within minutes …

Clearly, then, an ambivalent response. But just as I'd hoped, participating
in a project like this has altered some of that. Through it I have got to
know people, many of them writers, and it's been a great comfort. The
ochres and sages are beginning to fade. Not entirely though. I would
like to keep some of my outsider's vision, for all the confusion it's caused
me. Because even if we've lived our whole lives here, all the contibutors
to this volume are in a sense outsiders. That, at bottom, is what writers
need to be.

My thanks, then, both to the contributors and those who were unable
to contribute, but assured me that they would in the future should
another opportunity arise. A number of pieces were written specially
for this book, others are new versions of pieces that have appeared in
other publications, others of these have come to us unchanged. Whatever
their provenance, their authors have been amazingly generous, offering
what they had for no payment. For a generally poorly paid profession,
this was no mean thing.

There are one or two stories in this as well. Patrick Lane wanted to
give us something but the book he was working on was contracted to a
publisher who wouldn't let him publish any part of it before it appeared
in their book. Then Marion Farrant remembered a piece that Patrick
had written for a 1997 reading in the series that she and Pauline
Holdstock ran, and he agreed to our using that. Except that he couldn't
find it anywhere in his office or on his computer. Marion was convinced
that she'd received it as an email and proceeded to hunt for it among
her old messages, going so far as getting her husband Terry to put her
defunct computer together again to see if Patrick's piece was hidden
there. No luck, alas; so one of our most eminent writers is missing. So
too with Susan Mayse, also caught up in a book, and whose beautiful

piece about the Oyster River was just that, about the Oyster River. For us, that meant another disappointing lack.

Yet some of the most interesting contributions came from writers who are not so well known. There is Philip Kevin Paul's brilliant poem "The Water Drinker" out of his book of equally magnificent poems *Taking the Names down from the Hill*, and for which we made an exception to our prose stipulation, since it set the scene for the volume as nothing else could. And Barbara Powell's evocative mood piece about a widow taking comfort in her keenly observed environment. Michael Elcock's simple retelling of a flight across the Georgia Strait is a moving tribute to his pilot father. Charlotte Biscay tells a tale of a couple embarked on a rather offbeat quest. Margot E Coulter has let her imagination soar over Sidney's Beacon Avenue with "Olav's Story"; Sylvia Olsen has lifted a veil on peninsula life in her finely wrought "Anna's Medicine". In "Song Cycle" Anthony Taylor writes about another aspect of the peninsula entirely, how it was formed and what makes our coastline unique. Joan Coldwell's "The Park" is written with a deliciously dark sense of humour; Anny Scoones' "Pickled Eggs"with her own special brand of whimsy.

It came as no surprise to me that many of the pieces would be humourous, aware as I am that some of the most successful American comedians have been, in fact, Canadian. What was surprising was the variety. From Michael Cullen's madcap send-up of a visiting film crew to Rick Hudson's wry "Secrets" with all shades of satire in between, readers will find themselves laughing as I did as the pieces came in. Michael Coney has pulled off the remarkable feat of making a fable both funny and gripping. There's also the laughter of recognition: MAC Farrant's "Skidney"for one will have many readers nodding. Then there's Susan Musgrave's "The Gift" — vintage Musgrave, black and hilarious and blisteringly honest as ever.

For those who relish fine writing it is here in abundance. Not excluding the pieces already mentioned, there are others distinguished by their writers' sure feel for both storytelling and language. Lorna Crozier, famed throughout Canada for her poetry, has contributed a kind of miniature memoir in "Ghost Story", recording a Saskatchewan childhood and the adjustment required of her when coming to settle here. Margaret Thompson's elegant "Status Quo" takes a subtle poke at contagious suburban pomposities. Kathy Page, a former Londoner, has given us a sharply rendered account of the richness that lies behind apparently simple exteriors. In "Turn of the Year" Pauline Holdstock displays the deftness and sensitivity for which she is widely known. Stephen Hume offers a tribute to people of the peninsula, present and past.

Each contribution has its own distinct flavour, but, as might have been expected, there are common themes. The change in the peninsula's character from woodland to farmland to suburbia and the social dislocation this has caused. The relentless march of development. The dispossession of the Saanich people. The plight of the stranger seeking to adjust. Certain images recur. The benches in Sidney, the water, the rocky beaches, the mountains, the islands, the trees, the birds. To me, the awkward newcomer, it's been an inspiration to read the peninsula through these writers' works.

The writers come first but there are others who have made this book possible. We thank the British Columbia Arts Council, the Town of Sidney and the Districts of North and Central Saanich for their funding. Brenda Clarke and the directors of the Community Arts Council of the Saanich Peninsula for their unflagging support. Thanks too to Dianne Cross, the weaver with a vision, and the other members of the Council's Literature Committee: Christine Tanner, Marion Farrant, Pauline Holdstock, with special thanks to Christine for her invaluable advice and to Christine Toller of Orca Books.

We owe a big debt of gratitude to Kit McDonald, whose rendition of the gulf in "Sunrise from Tulista" so perfectly captured our themes, and who, like all the writers, was willing to let us use her work for free. To Janice Cook of Byword who did the typesetting and knows more now about fonts and quotation marks than she'd probably care to, our thanks, and to Abel Serfaty of A & E Print and Copy for more than a rush job.

Finally, we thank you, the readers, without whom no book can claim to exist.

WATER DRINKER

Philip Kevin Paul

The music in trees
is water. The only way

of learning that still counts:
I learned this summer
how a tree is a reflection
of a river or a stream.

A tree is like ancient love:
the love my parents gave me
came from a long ways away,
was divided over and over. *The oldest river*
will have the most branches.
It is the only thing
that remains uncomplicated,
grows outward and remains
uncomplicated.

How do you know these things?

The man, sick of the story and of his life, says:
I spent twelve years with the same river
measuring everything to learn
measuring is irrelevant.

There is only time
and looking.

After twelve years you can finally imagine
how a river grows old
and how the trees around it   grow old.

They grow outward and remain uncomplicated.

I sat by a fishless stream for days
this summer, the place I fished
when I was as small
as I remember being.
I felt in the heat the hope in me
being washed over and diluted.
I felt this way without knowing
the fish had all disappeared —

I'd imagined them all summer
swaying lazily in the dark,
murky water at the bottom of the stream
and the flash of their white bellies
as they twisted into the terrible light,
fighting at one end
of a handline.

Here—I bring you to the place
of maples, where on this steep hill
there is only one arbutus, the way
the blood from a fish looks
resting in the stones.

You can feel the stream
on that hill like a small animal
shaking in your hand. Its rhythm
comes up through the ground
just where the water is
about to roll over the edge.

Imagine what the Old People thought
when they saw one small red tree
growing between the grey-
white bodies of the maples.
Imagine their thoughts
when they realized
every stream has its own song
from the shape made by the trees around it,
the sound of the water
turning in the hollow,
returning to them from the leaves.

How long did they sit here
on this perfect flat rock beside
this single arbutus
to finally see
the trees around it were dying
because they weren't as deeply rooted?

When I tell you the word
is still old, I say that
because the first time
a man said ĶO, ĶO, IŁĆ,
said *water drinker*,
it was because the generations
before him had sat on the rock
and looked at the tree.
They sat in name of the tree,
as in a song too familiar
to hear, and finally
recognized it. And when
I say the word now, ĶO, ĶO, IŁĆ,
it is the same word,
but said in an alien light.

SECRETS

Rick Hudson

IF you live in a small community long enough, one of the things that will either drive you crazy or bring you peace of mind is the fact that everyone, sooner or later, gets to know everything there is to know about everyone else.

It can't be helped. No matter how hard you try to hide something, it'll come out in the end, one way or the other, and your darkest secrets are laid bare. For that reason, a lot of folks don't have any dark secrets, or if they do, they tend to mention them up front, with frills, at the earliest opportunity, so as to set the record straight, before someone else does it for them.

Yes, it's funny how the truth comes out, sooner or later. Sometimes, very much later. But, it comes out eventually. Maybe not in a large community, but in a place like Sidney there seems to be an inevitability about a secret that's as unstoppable as the forces of nature, the power of a river, the coming of winter, the pull of the tides … the truth will out.

Well, mostly, the truth will out.

Fact is, about the only time that the truth, the whole truth, and nothing but the truth failed to surface was … but maybe I should tell you how it happened, and let you make up your own mind.

Digger McClusky was a giant of a man, with a barrel for a

chest and a pair of hands on him that could break two-by-fours like they were kindling. Under a mop of ginger hair, he had a bush of ginger beard, and a temper to match them both. He made a living doing a bit of this, and a bit of that, but mostly he was a prospector. He'd worked just about every stream in the Chilcotin and Cassiar districts before he arrived on the Saanich Peninsula. That must have been about the same year Davey Williams finished high school.

McClusky showed up one day in a battered truck, with a broken backhoe on a trailer, and a pile of mining sieves and pumps and sluices and what-have-you tied on the back of both. That summer he panned or hydraulicked the upper reaches of the Sooke River. Then he worked the Loss Creek area for a while. He was slow and thorough, and he seemed to make enough to get by, but never enough to throw his hat in the air about anything.

He seldom appeared, and when he did, he didn't talk to folks much, except if he went into the Prairie Inn for a few. It became obvious pretty quickly that with a few whiskeys under his belt, Digger McClusky became a barbarian. When he was drunk, he had an opinion on everything, and woe betide the person who expressed a contrary belief. One night he threw Louis Tibault clear over the billiard table, because Louis suggested the Canadiens weren't the team they used to be. Witnesses said McClusky would have torn Louis' arms off, only a couple of guys got between them and calmed everything down. Still, Louis didn't go back to work for over a week.

After that, folks tended to drink up and leave whenever big Digger's frame appeared in the pub doorway. A month later he tore the door off one of those little Japanese imports, to prove they were only made of paint and plastic. After he'd had a few, mind. There were several witnesses. Was it possible? Could a human do that? So there was considerable relief in the community when he disappeared after a year, no doubt heading for another valley and another motherlode.

But the following summer he was back. Only now he wasn't alone. In his absence, McClusky had married, and when he reappeared, people were amazed. What those two saw in each other beat the band, it really did. He was lumbering and grotesque; she was like a fairy, light-limbed and delicate, dancing on the head of a pin. You could almost believe it, when someone suggested she was an elf.

Beauty and the Beast was how Ma Doughty summed them up, and as usual, she hit the nail right on the head. At any rate, Cecilia could soothe the savage beast in McClusky. Word quickly spread that he was off the sauce. That meant no fights. Everyone breathed more easily. When she was around, he would bend his huge frame and whisper in her ear, like a grizzly trying to snuggle into her lap, pretending to be a poodle.

The ladies loved it. They always do, because there's a strong feeling in the community that the female gender is vastly superior to the male. And what Cecilia McClusky had done for her husband simply proved it. When you saw them together, it was abundantly clear to anyone with the intelligence above a chainsaw, that she had tamed him.

But, while most of the guys chuckled privately that old Digger had sold out to the fair sex, there were a lot of fellows who remembered what had happened in the Prairie Inn, and to the Japanese import. There were murmurs about leopards never changing their spots, and old dogs not learning new tricks. Of course, they didn't express these views within earshot of Digger. He might just have forgotten that he was on a leash, and taken offence. And the last thing anyone wanted to see was an offended McClusky.

The arrival of a lady in his life domesticated him sufficiently that they rented acreage on the peninsula, with a small cottage. While Digger was away mucking and moiling, Cecilia planted a garden, and prettied up the place. When Digger was in town, which wasn't too often, they appeared at local events, like a softball game, and then a church picnic, and the Sidney Days

Barbecue. They got to be known quite well that summer. Still, folks didn't take to Digger too much. Being next to him was still like sitting next to a volcano — he was just so big, and those forearms were so muscled. You just never knew if or when he'd erupt.

Cecilia — now there was a different story! She was bewitching in every sense of the word. The ladies loved her, because she seemed to know all sorts of things that ladies need to know. She had cures for arthritis, and little bracelets for rheumatism. She knew all about herbs, and what cured winter colds, and which leaves made the best bouquet garni. She could spin, and sew, and made all her own clothes, and offered patterns and advice to anyone who asked for them. Her recipes were different and delicious, and she charmed people wherever she went.

The men found her attractive too. She could listen in a way that made a fellow feel he was saying the most important thing she had ever heard. She would turn her head slightly to one side, so her long auburn hair, braided with flowers, would cover one eye, and she would look up at him without saying a word. She had more men mesmerized by September than the playoffs did. Her eyes enticed and rebuffed at the same time. Her waist was impossibly narrow, and her ankles, often hidden below long, diaphanous skirts, had tiny bells on them that tinkled as she walked, so she seemed almost to be dancing on air.

Yes sir, the men found her attractive all right, and that's where things began to unravel. Buzz Sawyer started to drop over her place on occasions when Digger was away hydraulicking, and pretty soon, just as I said previously, in a place where there are no secrets, the whole place knew. Or, thought they knew.

Except Digger. It took him a while to find out. When he did, he went straight round to Buzz's place, rang his doorbell, and beat him up so badly Buzz couldn't work in the lumberyard until Christmas. No charges were laid.

Later that same evening, Digger was seen in the Prairie Inn, knocking them back hot and heavy. In fact, he was in there every night for a week. Nobody saw his elfin wife at all.

"It's none of our business," everyone said. "They gotta sort it out themselves."

I guess they did. When Cecilia appeared in the supermarket some time later, she had a bruised face, and walked with a limp. And there were no ankle bells.

Nobody said anything, mind. They didn't dare. "Don't take sides" is what folks murmured to each other from the safety of kitchen tables or over the phone.

As Thanksgiving rolled around, the prospecting business tapered off, and Digger and Cecilia were seen again. Near Halloween, Davey Williams heard a couple of ladies arguing about whether Cecilia was a witch.

"She knows a lot about plants and herbs," said one.

"And they say she goes into the forest by herself, even in winter," said another.

"She told Ma Doughty's fortune the other day," said the first with some conviction. "She was amazing! She knew everything about that woman."

"That's not difficult in a place like this!"

"But she knew things that Ma said she hardly knew herself!"

"Like what?"

"Well," said the storyteller, "she told Ma she had a sister. Only Ma said she didn't. You'd have thought that would have made Cecilia back down; but she didn't! She insisted Ma had a sister. Ma wouldn't have any of it. There was a kind of standoff, if you know what I mean. Nice and friendly, though. Then Cecilia said that Ma might not be remembering correctly, because the sister was dead!"

"No!"

"Yes!"

"And …"

"Well, Ma went pale, and said that now she thought about it, she *did* have a sister, only she'd died in childbirth years before Ma was born! She'd forgotten all about her."

"That's uncanny."

"How could she have known that, unless she was a witch?"

"Not a witch, dear. That sounds medieval. You mean, she's in touch with all her senses, and with the Earth."

"That's all a witch is, of course. She's just using her woman's intuition."

"Exactly."

"What else did she do?"

"I forget, now. She read Ma's fortune from the tea leaves in her cup. It was a lot of fun. We all had a good laugh. Only, the bit about the dead sister was strange."

"I hear she reads the tarot cards too."

"Oh, now I'd like to have my fortune read on the tarot cards."

"Me too."

"I can't think how she can live with that man," said one of them.

"The age difference!"

"Maybe," said the first with only half a giggle, "maybe he really is a bear, and she rides him at full moon!"

"One thing's certain," said another, "things have changed in that marriage. He's not half as nice to her as when they arrived last spring."

"She's either the most accident-prone woman around," muttered the second, "or he's beating her."

"No!"

"Sure! Look at the bruises on her arms. I saw them when she took off her coat at the Fergusons'. Of course, she covered them up quickly with a long-sleeved blouse!"

"Made it herself, she did."

"Lord, I wish I was half the seamstress she is. Her fingers are so quick and nimble. Did you see the embroidery on that blouse? It was a work of art!"

"Never mind the blouse. Did you see her colouring at the Waltons' last Saturday? That wasn't eye shadow; that was a bruise, as sure as I'm sitting here."

Davey Williams was eighteen then, and he was enchanted. Cecilia McClusky might be a witch! He'd never seen a witch before, but the sudden realization that she might be one put her in a completely different light. Not unfavourable, you understand. I mean, witches have had a bad rap from the Dark Ages right through to Walt Disney. Cecilia wasn't that kind of witch at all. She was the magical, good kind. It was so obvious, once you looked at her the right way.

He saw her in town a few days later, at the drugstore. When I say he saw her, what really happened was that he heard her. Those tinkling ankle bells carried across the aisles, so he suddenly knew, with absolute certainty, that she was right in front of him, separated only by a row of bottles and a divider board.

He caught his breath, and all sorts of wild thoughts flew through his head. Could she see through walls like Superman? Maybe she could smell him. Witches were supposed to have incredible senses of smell. Perhaps she could hear his breathing. No, he wasn't breathing. He was frozen, mesmerized. It felt as if even his heart had stopped beating.

With great effort, Davey forced himself to walk slowly to the end of the aisle. Once there, he casually leaned round to get a glimpse of her. It was Cecilia all right. She was half-turned away from him, reaching up to the topmost shelf so her long skirt rose almost to her calves. Her legs were tanned and slim and beautiful, he thought, and even though it was December, she still wore open sandals that showed her delicate feet. And ankle bells.

He realized he was staring, and looked away, but not before she turned and caught his eye. He blushed scarlet and stepped quickly back into the next aisle, confused and embarrassed. Without thinking, he left his half-full shopping basket right there, and blundered out into the street. His face was burning. It was difficult to breathe; he needed to be outside. He couldn't bear the thought of meeting her again.

But meet her again, he did. Some weeks later, he was hunting ducks up-island. Returning to his pick-up about mid-morning, there was Digger's truck parked in the clearing. It gave him a nasty scare. I mean, the guy had almost killed Louis, and his wife was a witch. He wasn't the sort of guy you wanted to run into on a remote trail.

Davey dropped his birds quickly into the back of his vehicle, but just as he opened the door, he heard the bells, faint but clear on the crisp morning air. A strange lethargy seemed to grip him, and he could not, for the life of him, pull himself up into the cab of the truck. His left foot had frozen to the ground.

She walked into the clearing wrapped in a fur-lined parka, clasping an armful of plants. A cap hid the mass of auburn hair, but nothing could hide the glow that radiated from her face as she walked toward him, smiling. She didn't seem the slightest bit surprised to see him there.

"Hello," she said in a voice that sent hot shivers down his spine. He smiled weakly. There was no way his voice could function. He didn't trust himself to say anything.

She came close, pulling off her cap and shaking out the tangles in her hair. It struck him suddenly that she didn't look much older than he was. Today, she wasn't wearing sandals — it was too cold — but her boots barely left a mark on the frost-covered ground. Davey wondered again whether maybe she really was a witch. Witches could fly. The tinkling bells were tied to the embroidered tops of her boots.

Up very close, her eyes were enchanting, and Davey couldn't stop looking at them. They were a very pale gray, almost white like a malamute's, but they seemed to have a depth of understanding quite out of keeping with the youthfulness of her face.

"Look what I've found," she said. She held up her plants for him to admire. Davey smiled again, still unable to speak, his heart pounding.

She didn't appear put out by his silence. She half turned away from him, so her back was almost against his chest, and he had to look over her shoulder at the leaves. Then, very softly, as though she was explaining to a child, she told him the names and uses of each herb and plant she had collected. Every now and then she turned her face up into his, to see if he was paying attention.

Heck, Davey confessed years later, he couldn't have moved just then, even if a CPR freight train had been coming straight on, and they were on the tracks. Mesmerized, that's what he was.

When she finished, she skipped away, as though suddenly shy to be so close to him in such remote surroundings. She peered into the back of his truck, and saw the broken bundle of ducks. Her face fell, and she leaned over the side and touched one of them.

"They're warm," she said, and looked at him. Davey felt terrible, and wished wildly that he'd never shot any of them. She looked at the birds again, the bright plumage splayed out across the rusty metal floor. Her fingers caressed the long pinion feathers of a wing. The look of sadness passed.

"You must be a real good shot," she said, smiling.

"I guess." They were the first words he'd spoken.

"Do you often hunt here?"

"Once or twice each fall. Sometimes it's good. Sometimes not."

"Do you hunt alone?"

"I guess."

"Is that safe? What if you had an accident?"

Davey grinned foolishly. "I dunno."

"Don't you have friends to come with?" she asked, looking sideways with those enchanting eyes. He felt his chest tighten up again.

"Not really." Davey knew what he wanted to say, but his voice wasn't capable of saying it.

She seemed to read his thoughts. "You're a loner, aren't you." It wasn't a question. Before he could think of anything to say to that, she said, "I'm a loner too, you know." She turned and smiled at him with that come-here, go-away smile of hers that made his head spin. "We're both loners."

There was nothing Davey could think to say to that. She turned back to the ducks again, and touched one of them gently. For a crazy second, he thought she was willing it back to life. The way he felt at that moment, he would gladly have watched her work a miracle with each dead bird, and watch them all fly away.

She looked at her fingers. The tip of her index had a spot of blood on it. She walked up to Davey with a curiously determined stride. He didn't know what she was going to do, but he was powerless to defend himself. She reached up and touched Davey's forehead with her bloodied finger; he felt the stickiness on his skin. Then she did an even stranger thing. She touched her own forehead, leaving a pale red dot there too.

"Loners," she said, and her eyes were deep and beautiful.

Then she was gone. Davey heard her truck start. He managed to wave goodbye as she drove out of the clearing, but it was a long time before he could climb into the cab of his pick-up.

Spring came early the following year. Digger left for the Sooke Hills, leaving his elfin wife behind. The ladies called round, and were supportive. The men stayed well clear. There was a big T standing over that cottage, and it stood for Trouble. Even if Digger was out of town.

Davey Williams was helping with the spring clean-up at the daffodil farm. It was dirty work, and long hours. Most evenings he got a ride home, but one evening he worked late. After he finished, he washed up and then faced the five-k walk to Central Saanich in the dark.

It was a calm, unseasonably warm night. The ground had thawed under a spring sun, and there were smells of loam and earth that touched the nostrils, and plucked at the senses, making it good to be alive, and alone, and walking along the farm track under a big, three-quarter moon.

That same moon shone down on the McClusky cottage, where early daffodils were just budding in the garden. Davey knew that, because he saw them as he approached along the road. As he came closer, he thought he heard a strange, melodious singing coming from nowhere and everywhere, like echoes in a deep canyon. But when the sound of the gravel crunching under his boots stopped, nothing reached his straining ears. There was no light in the window. Davey paused and leaned over the fence for a while, just drinking in the quiet stillness of the place.

You couldn't ignore the magical quality of the night. A special aura enveloped Cecilia's garden, where in the summer she grew herbs and practised her secret potions. It made a fellow wonder if magic really could exist alongside DVDs and screw-top beer.

Thinking about it later, he couldn't be sure when exactly he became aware that she was there. Her presence just seemed to grow on his consciousness. Perhaps it was the soft tinkling of the ankle bells that did it. Next thing he knew, she was beside him at the fence, leaning out over the top rail in the same way he was leaning in. Her hair was undone and floated about her in the moonlight, although there was no wind. The air was so still it seemed that spring was holding its breath, waiting. Waiting for what? Davey wondered.

"Hello," she said in her soft voice. She didn't appear surprised that he was leaning over her fence in the late evening, under a silver moon. Davey smiled shyly. Nothing he could say came even close to describing how he felt just then.

She took a step closer to him along the rail, so their elbows almost touched. "I'm glad you came," she said simply. She smelled of apple blossom, and her bare arms looked silver in the light. Davey was struck dumb.

Then she spoke for both of them, and the things she revealed were wonderful and magical, and full of promise beyond all his dreams. Her voice whispered to him, so he was drawn along like a leaf in a stream, until the stream became a river and then the river became a flood. And Davey, the leaf, was carried along on the surface far, far away from everything he knew, into different worlds of mystic lands and distant places, as yet undreamed of. Later, she stood in front of him, so that they were almost intertwined, and yet not touching at all, and she whispered dark and delicious things that he had never heard before.

After what seemed like an infinity of time, she took his hand in hers. Her skin was so smooth around his calloused fingers that he wanted to hold onto her forever. And she told him other things, wild things, terrible things, but when she told them, they seemed neither wild nor terrible. He leaned against the rail under the three-quarter moon, and listened to her soft voice and what she said, and heard the gentle tinkling of the ankle bells when she moved.

Then she opened his hand with her delicate fingers that smelled of apple blossom, and she pressed a pebble into his palm. It was heavy and coarse, and scratched his hardened skin. Davey wanted to say something, anything, to tell her what he thought, but he couldn't. Instead, he pulled back from the fence, away from her beguiling, silvery form, and with his remaining strength he staggered back to the edge of the road.

He strode away from that place toward the town with its lights, and the noise of trucks without mufflers, and dogs barking in back yards. Later, he couldn't remember anything about the walk. When next he noticed where he was, it was to find himself back in his room, in the security of his own place.

Six weeks later, big Digger McClusky was shot stone-cold dead, after he'd left the Prairie Inn late one night. The Mounties moved pretty quickly, and charged a young drifter, who had an illegal forty-five and no real motive. He didn't deny he'd done it. He said that Digger was about to knock his head off, and he'd shot in self-defence. There were no witnesses.

Cecilia was heartbroken, and went into mourning. She might not have liked living with her husband that much, but she could scarcely bear the thought of living without him. She didn't want to see anyone, speak to anyone, be comforted by anyone.

When it went to trial, it was a big affair. The biggest thing on the peninsula in years, everyone said. The charges were possession of an illegal weapon and second-degree murder.

A high profile lawyer from Vancouver defended the young drifter, Judge Smith presiding. The crown tried to prove a link between Digger, the boy and McClusky's mining operations. They suggested that Digger had hit pay dirt, and the drifter had found out about it. To prove their case, they produced exhibit A, a gold chain belonging to the boy. There was a four-ounce gold nugget in a locket that he'd been wearing at the time of the shooting.

The defence pointed out there are thousands of lockets with gold nuggets in them, worn by countless people in the province. There was no proof the nugget had come from Digger's property. Furthermore, the kid had an alibi right up until the week he'd arrived on the peninsula, and McClusky had been out of town, at his claim, the whole time the boy was around. The defence proved pretty convincingly that before the night of the shooting, they'd never met.

The Prairie Inn barman was called to testify. He'd been behind the counter on the night of McClusky's death. No, he hadn't seen the drifter. Yes, Digger had been drinking. No, he hadn't threatened anyone; there hadn't been many folks in that night. Yes, McClusky might have been drunk when he left the bar. Everyone looked at Cecilia McClusky, and their hearts ached.

The defence called Louis Tibault, who described in hushed whispers what Digger had done to him. Louis held up a crooked left hand to show the judge the consequences of crossing Digger McClusky. Most of the jury didn't look.

The crown came back to the motive. The drifter hadn't killed McClusky out of self-defence, they contended. He'd done it for money. Digger had struck it rich, and somehow, the boy had found out.

It didn't wash. In a place like ours, it only took a couple of witnesses to convince Judge Smith that there was no way a gold strike could be kept quiet. There were no secrets. McClusky was broke at the time of his death. His bank account, his possessions, and his wife's tearful testimony confirmed that.

They kept Cecilia in the witness box for less than fifteen minutes, and everyone who was there felt her loss. She deserved better from life, they all said. She never once looked at the young man who had shot her husband. He looked at her with pain in his eyes.

In wrapping up, the defence pleaded the accused's youth, and his previous clean record. It was an act of self-defence, the lawyer argued, looking at the jury squarely, by a young man in a strange town, facing a giant. The jury debated for less than an hour. The drifter got four years for manslaughter, and one year for possession of an illegal weapon, both sentences to run concurrently.

Digger's wife sat dark-eyed through the whole affair, dressed in black, silent, staring. No bells tinkled from her ankles. Like many of the folks there, she seemed shocked by the verdict. Shortly after the trial, she packed up and disappeared. There were no goodbyes. One day she was there, the next she was gone, without a forwarding address.

Folks were sorry to see her go. While her husband had been wild, everyone liked Cecilia. Her lightness and charm had convinced skeptics and admirers alike that she'd paid a heavy price for getting hitched up with Digger McClusky. People admired her courage. One or two of the guys were in love with her. That was plain, though it hadn't surfaced during the trial.

What also hadn't come out at the trial, for the simple reason that nobody had asked, was that Davey Williams felt humiliated and guilty. Humiliated, because Cecilia McClusky had been forced to ask a complete stranger to do what he, Davey, had refused to do; and guilty, because the pebble she'd pressed into his hand that magical evening was a gold nugget weighing many ounces.

STATUS QUO

Margaret Thompson

HEAVY footsteps race across the roof, followed immediately by a resounding thud and a scrabbling, dragging noise.

"Hello, Percy," says Lucy, turning her head away from her computer just in time to catch the peacock skidding to a halt at the balcony railing. He is a frequent visitor, addicted to Lucy's home-made wholewheat bread. She finds him companionable.

Percy screams.

"It's no good, you know," says Lucy. "They've gone."

And I know what that feels like, she thinks, *but you get over it eventually.*

The bird screams again, a desperate sound that rips the fabric of the air.

And then again, Lucy thinks, *it can still hurt.*

Percy makes a clumsy hop onto the railing and starts preening. His iridescent blue neck contorts as he twists his head round to peer intently into his wing feathers, exactly as if he is stalking game, before a quick stab buries his beak in down.

"That's right," says Lucy to the bird. "It's important to keep up appearances."

It had been the peacock, rather than the realtor, who had sold Lucy on the house in the quiet cul-de-sac. She had gasped at the view of Haro Strait, Mount Baker directly opposite, its snowy flanks brilliant in the sun, when she had first seen it through the huge picture windows. The garden appealed to her, especially the apple tree with its inviting limbs; she liked the way the slope seemed to meld with the grassy acreage below, and ultimately with the farm fields along Lochside Drive, giving her the heady feeling that she owned everything as far as the eye could see. Even the design of the house, conventional though it was, fired her imagination.

"We could rent out the bottom floor and bring in a little extra," she whispered to Sam as they took in the completely separate apartment downstairs.

But it was the peacock which had clinched matters. The first time she saw it, Lucy watched in disbelief as the gaudy creature paced in a measured fashion down the street, veering off to take a shortcut through a hedge into a neighbouring garden.

"*Alice in Wonderland*," she murmured. "And I'm Alice."

"What're you on about?" asked Sam.

Alice would have been a closed book to Sam, literally. It was always such hard work to explain those references to him.

"Nothing," she said. "Who does he belong to?"

The realtor thought the bird was a free agent, wandering at will about the area, and that was indeed the case.

"There's another one somewhere," she said. "I've seen it further down the hill. Gorgeous, aren't they?"

Yes, thought Lucy, *and I want to live where peacocks roam as if they belong.*

Sam made an offer that night, happy to avoid weeks of househunting. By the end of the week, they had their retirement home.

After pacing up and down the balcony rail and bobbing several times as if nerving himself to jump, the peacock launches himself into space. Lucy watches as the bird glides down, tail feathers rippling behind him, just clears the fence at the bottom of the garden and lands halfway down the neighbour's field.

She still feels a bit guilty about putting up the fence, but gives a little nod of satisfaction as she surveys her garden. So different now from the lumpy grass and stark rectangular beds filled with neglected strawberry plants she started with.

"It's a work of art, Lucy!" her friend Loranne had said on her last visit. "What a pity Sam never saw it."

But flowers weren't really his thing, thinks Lucy, and frowns as the noise of a leaf blower somewhere to her right, behind the grove of trees at the end of the road, mars the afternoon.

After years of logging round Prince George, Sam had looked forward to the Island's climate. His attempts to grow fruit trees in the north had limited success; the trees that were hardy enough to survive the punishing cold often fell victim to bears, who tore down whole branches to gorge on the fruit, wrecking years of slow growth in one impatient tug. Sam's persistence in the face of these obstacles seemed almost pathological at times, to Lucy.

As soon as they moved in, he had dragged Lucy out to the garden to pick out the best places for his fruit trees. Then they made the rounds of all the garden centres, Sam marvelling all the while at how many there were, how much choice he had.

"Bit different from Art Knapp's and nothing else, eh?" he asked triumphantly as he selected a Cox's Orange, two pear trees, and a cherry with five different species grafted onto one trunk. He also got two peaches. "They'll be perfect on that wall at the side," he crowed.

Lucy wondered privately what he needed them all for. Every fruit known to man grew within a mile of their house, it seemed. Any more trees, and she could give up the idea of flowers, not to mention a view.

Sam's frenzied digging and planting brought about a first encounter with the next-door neighbours in the drab Panabode, whose name was Chatterton, though how they learned this Lucy never knew, for nobody made any introductions. People certainly kept to themselves, she found.

An elderly man in a cloth cap was sitting on an upturned box under his balcony, smoking a pipe. He grunted reluctantly when Sam hailed him and made no effort to prolong the conversation. Sam had given up, muttering "Miserable old bastard!" under his breath, and returned to digging a hole for the cherry, when the old man shuffled up behind him.

"What's that you're putting in there?" he asked.

Sam told him.

Mr. Chatterton sniffed. "Close to the property line," he said, and turned away, lobbing a Parthian shot over his shoulder. "Hope you know where your septic field is."

It was all academic, anyway. A few days later Lucy heard a howl of rage from the garden and hurried out to find Sam, apoplectic, grieving over his infant trees.

"Goddam deer!" he spluttered. "Came out and found it standing there, chewing the last leaf off my cherry. The last leaf!"

The deer had evidently enjoyed all the others, too.

"And that old misery watched me put them in, and didn't say a word about deer! Right neighbourly, I call that!"

Lucy hadn't known that deer were commonplace on the peninsula, but now she kept seeing them, drifting across the fields, striding down the road, pushing their way under hedges and shrubs. The list of plants labelled "deerproof" in the garden centres began to make sense, although it was quite obvious that the animals themselves had never read it; they happily consumed her tomato plants one night.

That was the origin of the fence. Lucy regretted cutting off access; she could imagine the deer's bewilderment as their range had slowly shrunk over the years. But Sam was determined, and refused to encase his trees in protective mesh.

"It would look awful," he insisted, "besides that's not all they'd go for. Are you going to cover *everything* with chicken wire?"

Lucy capitulated and Sam threw himself into construction

until an eight-foot wire fence surrounded their garden. He was satisfied with it — "Let them try getting over that!" he said — but Lucy thought it looked rude and harsh. She found herself mentally listing vines and creepers that would cover it up.

The Chattertons also disliked it. As soon as Sam had finished, they were out to inspect the post he'd put in at the bottom corner of the hedge between the gardens, scrabbling about to uncover the surveyor's marker. Mr Chatterton wasn't able to complain that Sam had crossed the line, but he found a grievance.

"How's a man to prune the hedge?" he asked the air.

Lucy thought that a man could well do it the way he always had, by asking permission to come into their garden, but she kept silent. The Chattertons got their own back when pruning time came. They sheared only their own side of the hedge and pushed the clippings from the top into Lucy's garden.

But building the fence seemed to take the steam out of Sam. Lucy worried about his lethargy, and tried to buck him up by taking him to choose some more trees. He did select another cherry, but it soon became another source of guilt for Lucy. The morning he decided to plant it, she found him collapsed over a half-dug hole when she went to call him in for lunch. He had snapped the tree in half in his fall.

That evening, Lucy is intrigued to see strange cars parked along what Mrs Chatterton always called "the boulevard". From her spare bedroom window, she watches a group of young men and women spill from three vehicles — the sort Sam would have called clunkers — and converge on a U-Haul van parked in the driveway of the house opposite.

The road, normally quite dead by that time of the evening, echoes with their voices as they carry box after box into the house, lug chairs, tables and mattresses, lamps trailing flexes and two huge rubber plants in terracotta pots. They take more and more frequent rest breaks; decrepit loungers soon appear on the patio, as well as a battered blue cooler apparently full of beer.

By ten-thirty it is more party than work. The voices rise in competition with the music; a relentless bass thumps and pounds as if the night itself has developed migraine. Lucy retreats to the back of her house, where the noise is mercifully muted, and tries to be tolerant of the newcomers.

Youngsters, she thinks, *having fun, no idea how the sound carries.* But a distant sound of breaking glass, and a jeering, hooting hullabaloo make her frown. *I hope this doesn't become a habit*, she says to herself.

Mrs Chatterton certainly wouldn't have approved, but then, she rarely did. Lucy fared no better with her than Sam had with Mr Chatterton. Together, it seemed, as the oldest residents, the Chattertons had appointed themselves the moral guardians of the street.

Lucy had found this out through experience and observation. Her first clash with Mrs Chatterton had come just before noon one Saturday in March when she had hurried outside to burn up some garden rubbish. She had just got the fire burning well in the barrel.

"Burning's illegal after twelve on a Saturday, you know."

Lucy turned. Mrs Chatterton, hands on wide navy-blue hips, stood on her own balcony. Lucy knew the bylaw perfectly well, but temporized.

"Oh," she said lamely, "I started it before noon."

"Not by much."

Watching, were you? thought Lucy. "Not much I can do now," she said. "It'll be out soon."

Lucy's friend, Loranne, who lived on the other side of the Chattertons, had her own stories to tell.

"First they bitched about us planting a cedar hedge between the houses. Well, I said, if they'd stop spying on us through binoculars, for heaven's sake, we'd have no need of something tall to block their view! There they were, up on their balcony with binoculars, all the time we were building our pond. God knows what law they thought we were going to break — I wouldn't be surprised if they took photos, too. Evidence!"

Inevitably, the Chattertons had no time for the peacocks.

"I'm surprised you'd let that bird up there," Mrs Chatterton commented one day as Lucy scrubbed the deck on her balcony. "Dirty things, messing everywhere."

"Nowhere as bad as seagulls," said Lucy, "all that white splatter."

Mrs Chatterton reddened and walked away.

Lucy could imagine Mrs Chatterton's disgust when some other residents took pity on the peacock's lonely male splendour one day, and introduced a peahen into their back yard. She herself laughed out loud for the first time in months as she watched Percy hurtle off the neighbours' roof and race down the garden in pursuit of the female. The peahen feigned indifference, despite Percy's calls and excited posturing. He ran to and fro in front of her, twirled his fan and rear end in her face, while she kept walking downhill, pretending to find delectable titbits on the ground as she went. Finally, they disappeared through a hedge.

Lucy had felt happy at Percy's awakened purpose in life, but it didn't last. The other peacock materialized and eloped with the female. Percy was alone once more.

"Good," said Mrs Chatterton. "We don't want to be overrun with birds eating every plant in sight."

She turned her attention to the peahen suppliers next; the number of vehicles parked outside their house on the boulevard made her suspect they were renting out a basement suite, illegal in Saanich, though people did it all the time. But it was not her finest hour; the Wilsons were billeting members of an international rowing team, and called her bluff by insisting that she inspect the house and meet the rowers. They also resented being called liars to their faces, and Mrs Chatterton was forced to apologize.

At about the same time, Mr Chatterton died. Nobody really noticed, which made Lucy feel guilty again.

Maybe he finally choked on his own bile, thought Lucy. *I wonder what sort of difference it will make to her?*

Lucy sits in her garden, eating her lunch. They are haying in the fields below the house and the steady thumping hum of the bailer fills the air. Her brand new neighbours are slapping paint on the dingy Panabode. On the whole, Lucy thinks they may be all right. They have hung a basketwork chair in the old pear tree and rooted out the brambles in Mr Chatterton's long-neglected vegetable patch. The house will always be a wooden box, but soon it will be a sage-green box rather than chocolate-pudding brown.

Loranne saunters down to sit with her; together they munch Ritz crackers and watch the last of the sage green going up next door.

"Thank God they've changed the colour," says Loranne. "Sort of erases the Chattertons at last, doesn't it?"

"Be fair," says Lucy, "she was never as bad once he'd gone."

"True, but now I don't feel as if I'm being *judged* all the time and found wanting."

"Yes," laughs Lucy, "we were all pretty unsatisfactory, weren't we!"

After her husband's death, Mrs Chatterton seemed to mellow. She actually sought human contact. She took to waylaying Lucy as she came out in the morning to collect her *Times Colonist*. Lucy got used to her neighbour's lengthy monologues, all delivered in her machine-gun delivery, with no pauses for response or change of subject.

"I don't know what they think they're doing up there," she began one morning, assuming Lucy would know immediately that she was talking about the people who had bought the huge lot beyond the trees at the dead end of the road, the place where the deer hid from the sun and the peacocks roosted. But then, the din of chainsaws and the heavy trucks grinding down the road at all hours had been the hot topic for weeks. "They're in trouble with Saanich, cutting down all those trees, even the ones they'd marked to be left standing, now it looks as if they're hoping to get an access road into *this* road as well as down below, but that would mean going over a bit of their neighbours' property and they're so annoyed about the trees they won't let them, or so I've heard, nothing's the same now, it used to be such a quiet road, just a few houses, always nice people here then, my father was the very first to come here when it was all a holly farm, his house is the one opposite you, rented out now, what do you think of those people in there now, make too much noise, I told the owner, but he's way over in Regina, never comes out here, doesn't mean a thing to him as long as there's someone paying him rent, so that's all she wrote, that's all I can tell you."

It didn't seem to occur to Mrs Chatterton that she had insulted Lucy as well as the renters by lamenting the decline in the quality of the residents. In fact, she seemed to have adopted Lucy as a confederate, if not an actual fellow spirit. She reported with glee her discovery that the imposing stone gateposts on the new house had been built just too narrow to permit the passage of a fire engine, should one ever be needed, and that the garbage man refused to collect their garbage if the gates were left locked. She knew everything: who owned what, who worked where, who owed money, whose children were in trouble. Most of all, though, she resurrected the past, when she had first come to the road as a young bride, long before any houses were built, long before there was a highway across the peninsula, long before other people came to flout all the rules and trample her rights and ignore her authority.

Why, she's just like Canute trying to turn back the tide, thought Lucy. *No wonder she's always in a rage!*

Lucy thought her neighbour would go on forever, finally drying up and being found one day, a little desiccated husk still peering out of her window. But Mrs Chatterton injured herself quite badly trying to take down a small flowering cherry in her front garden because it was, as she said, deformed (it leaned, rather gracefully, and looked delightfully Japanese, Lucy always thought.) She disappeared into hospital and was apparently shipped straight from there into a seniors' home. A son, who had never appeared before, came and cleared out the house, and the next day, a realtor's sign went up on Mrs Chatterton's front lawn. The realtor, a plump blonde with stiletto heels and long red fingernails, nailed it to the remains of the cherry tree.

"By the way," says Loranne, "have you seen what's gone up at the end of the road? Where Mr Gregory's old shack is?"

Lucy shook her head. Loranne was referring to the large overgrown lot at the other end of the street. Mr Gregory had lived there in squalid contentment for years until his daughter had swept him away to be "properly looked after". He had never made the slightest attempt at landscaping, never mown the grass; his lot was the nearest thing to virgin prairie anywhere on the island. He had also never owned a car, never went out and nobody had the slightest idea what he lived on.

"You should go and see," says Loranne. "There's one of those big boards developers put up. I don't like the look of it."

Lucy investigates after Loranne goes home. There is indeed a board. FOR SALE it reads. 4.5 ACRES FOR CONDO DEVELOPMENT.

As Lucy stands there gazing at the flattened grass, and the dilapidated wooden shack in the middle of it, windows shattered and the roof line sagging ominously, it seems to her that the noise from the highway is much louder than usual. A police car howls by, closely followed by an ambulance, someone else's emergency slipping heedlessly in and out of her life.

A dismal hoot startles her. Percy, she sees, is perched on the shack's broken porch rail. He has lost all his tail feathers and looks truncated.

"You don't like it either, eh? So what are we going to do about it? Got any money?"

Percy hoots again. It sounds like a protest.

Surely this is part of the Land Reserve, thinks Lucy. *There must be someone we can talk to about this.*

THE BYRDS
Michael Coney

GRAN started it all.

Late one afternoon in the hottest summer in living memory, she took off all her clothes, carefully painted red around her eyes and down her cheeks, chin and throat, painted the rest of her body a contrasting black with the exception of her armpits and the inside of her wrists which she painted white, strapped on her new antigravity belt, flapped her arms and rose into the nearest tree, a garry oak, where she perched.

She informed us that, as of now, she was a Rufous-necked Hornbill, of India.

"She always wanted to visit India," Gramps told us.

Gran said no more, for the logical reason that hornbills are not talking birds.

"Come down, Gran!" Mother called. "You'll catch your death of cold."

Gran remained silent. She stretched her neck and gazed out over the roofs of Sidney, doubtless in the direction of India.

"She's crazy," Father said. "She's crazy. I always said she was. I'll call the asylum."

"You'll do no such thing!" Mother was always very sensitive about Gran's occasional peculiarities. "She'll be down soon. The evenings are drawing in. She'll get cold."

"What's an old fool her age doing with an antigravity unit anyway, that's what I want to know," Father asked.

The Capital Regional District was restricting water supplies and the weatherman was predicting floods. BC Hydro was screaming for conservation due to excessive use of air conditioners, Canada Rest had announced that the population must fall by one point eight percent by November or else, the Mailgift was spewing out a deluge of application forms, tax forms and final reminders, the Tidy Mice were malfunctioning so that the house stank …

And now this.

It was humiliating and embarrassing, Gran up a tree, naked and painted. She stayed there all evening, and my girlfriend Pandora would be dropping by soon and would be sure to ask questions. The human race was at that point in the morality cycle when nudity was considered indecent. Gran was probably thirty years before or after her time. There was something lonely and anachronistic about her, perched there, balancing unsteadily in a squatting position, occasionally grabbing at the trunk for support then flapping her arms to re-establish the birdlike impression. She looked like some horrible mutation. Her resemblance to a Rufous-necked Hornbill was slight.

"Talk her down, Gramps," Father said.

"She'll come down when she's hungry."

Gramps was wrong. Late in the evening Gran winged her way to a vacant lot where an ancient tree stood. She began to eat unsterilized apples, juice flowing down her chin. It was a grotesque sight.

"She'll be poisoned!" Mother cried.

"So, she's made her choice at last," Father said. He was referring to *Your Choice for Peace*, a brochure which Gran and Gramps received monthly from Canada Rest. Accompanying the brochure is a six-page form on which senior citizens describe all that is good about their life in two languages, and a few of the things which bug them. At the end of the form is a box in which the oldster indicates his preference for Life or for Peace. If he does not check the box, or if he fails to complete the form, it is assumed that he has chosen Peace, and they send the Wagon for him.

Now Gran was cutting a picturesque silhouette against the pale blue of the evening sky as she circled the Sidney rooftops uttering harsh cries. She flew with arms outstretched, legs trailing, and we all had to admit to the beauty of the sight; that is, until a flock of starlings began to mob her. Losing directional control she spiralled downwards, recovered, levelled out and skimmed towards us, outpacing the starlings and regaining her perch in the garry oak. She made preening motions and settled down to roost the night away. The family Pesterminator, zapping bugs with its tiny laser, considered her electronically for a second but held its fire.

We were indoors by the time Pandora arrived. She was nervous, complaining that there was a huge mutation in the tree outside, and it had cawed at her.

Mother said quickly, "It's only a Rufous-necked Hornbill."

"A rare visitor to these shores," Father added.

"Why couldn't she have been a sparrow?" Mother asked, "or something else inconspicuous." Things were not going well for her. The little robot Tidy Mice still sulked behind the wainscoting and she'd had to clean the house by hand.

The garish Gran shone like a beacon in the morning sunlight. There was no concealing the family's degradation. A small crowd had gathered and people were trying to tempt Gran down with bread crumbs. She looked none the worse for her night out, and was greeting the morning with shrill yells.

Gramps was strapping on an antigravity belt. "I'm going up to fetch her down. This has gone far enough."

I said, "Be careful. She may attack you."

"Don't be a damned fool." Nevertheless Gramps went into the tool shed, later emerging nude and freshly painted. Mother uttered a small scream of distress, suspecting that Gramps, too, had become involved in the conspiracy to diminish the family's social standing.

I reassured her. "She's more likely to listen to one of her own kind."

"Has everyone gone totally insane?" Mother asked.

Gramps rose gracefully into the garry oak, hovered, then settled beside Gran. He spoke to her quietly for a moment and she listened, head cocked attentively.

Then she made low gobbling noises and leaned against him. He called down, "This may take longer than I thought."

"Oh, my God!" Mother exclaimed.

"That does it," Father said. "I'm calling her analyst."

Dr Pratt was tall and dignified, and he took in the situation at a glance. "Has your mother exhibited birdish tendencies before?"

Father answered for Mother. "No more than anyone else. Although, in many other ways she was —"

"Gran has always been the soul of conformity," Mother said quickly, beginning to weep. "If our neighbours have been saying otherwise I'll remind them of the slander laws. No — she did it to shame us. She always hated the colours we painted the house — she said it looked like a strutting peacock."

"Rutting peacock," Father corrected her. "She said rutting peacock. Those were her exact words."

"Peacock, eh?" Dr Pratt looked thoughtful. There was a definite avian thread running through this. "So you feel she may be acting in retaliation. She thinks you have made a public spectacle of the house in which she lives, so now she is going to make a public spectacle of you."

"Makes sense," Father said.

"Gran!" Dr Pratt called. She looked down at us, beady little eyes ringed with red. "I have the personal undertaking of your daughter and son-in-law that the house will be repainted in colours of your own choosing." He spoke on for a few minutes in soothing tones. "That should do it," he said to us finally, picking up his bag. "Put her to bed and keep her off berries, seeds, anything like that. And don't leave any antigravity belts lying around. They can arouse all kinds of prurient interests in older people."

"She still isn't coming down," Father pointed out. "I don't think she understood."

"Then I advise you to fell the tree." Dr Pratt's patience evaporated. "She's a disgusting old exhibitionist who needs to be taught a lesson. Just because she chooses to act out her fantasies in an unusual way doesn't make her any different from anyone else. And what's *he* doing up there, anyway? Does he resent the house paint as well?"

"He *chose* the paint. He's there to bring her down."

We watched them in perplexity. The pair huddled together on the branch, engaged in mutual grooming. The crowd outside on Resthaven Avenue had swollen to over a hundred.

The following morning Gran and Gramps greeted the dawn with a cacophony of gobbling and screeching. I heard Father throw open his bedroom window and threaten to blast them right out of that goddamned tree and into the hereafter if they didn't keep it down. I heard the metallic click as he cocked his twelve bore. I heard Mother squeal with apprehension, and the muffled thumping of a physical struggle in the next room.

I was saddened by the strain it puts on marriages when in-laws live in the house — or, in our case, outside the window.

The crowds gathered early and it was quickly apparent that Gramps was through with trying to talk Gran down; in fact, he was through with talking altogether. He perched beside his mate in spry fashion, jerking his head this way and that as he scanned the sky for hawks, cocking an eye at the crowd, shuddering suddenly as though shaking feathers into position.

Dr Pratt arrived at noon, shortly before the media. "A classic case of regression to the childlike state," he told us. "The signs are all there: the unashamed nakedness, the bright colours, the speechlessness, the favourite toy, in this case the antigravity belt. I have brought a surrogate toy which I think will solve our problem. Try luring them down with this."

He handed Mother a bright red plastic baby's rattle. Gran fastened a beady eye on it, shuffled her arms, then launched herself from the tree in a swooping glide. As Mother ducked in alarm, Gran caught the rattle neatly in her bony old toes, wheeled and flapped back to her perch. Heads close, she and Gramps examined the toy.

We waited breathlessly. Then Gran stomped it against the branch and the shattered remnants fell to the ground. The crowd applauded. For the first time we noticed the Victoria Newspocket van, and the crew with cameras. The effect on Dr Pratt was instantaneous. He strode towards them and introduced himself to a red-haired woman with a microphone.

"Tell me, Dr Pratt, to what do you attribute this phenomenon?"

"The manifestation of birdishness in the elderly is a subject which has received very little study up to the present date. Indeed, I would say that it has been virtually ignored. Apart from my own paper — still in draft form — you could search the psychiatric archives in vain for mention of Pratt's Syndrome."

"And why is that, Dr Pratt?"

"Basically, *fear*. The fear in each and every one of us of admitting that something primitive and atavistic can lurk within our very genes. For what is more primitive than a bird, the only survivor of the age of dinosaurs?"

"What indeed, Dr Pratt."

"You see in that tree two pathetic human creatures who have reverted to a state which existed long before Man took his first step on Earth, a state which can only have been passed on as a tiny coded message in their very flesh and the flesh of their ancestors, through a million years of Time."

"And speaking of time, how long do you expect their

condition to last, Dr Pratt?"

"Until late fall. The winters in southern Vancouver Island can be cold and wet, and they'll be out of that tree come the end of October, if they've got any sense left at all."

"Well, thank you, Dr —"

A raucous screaming cut her short. A group of shapes appeared in the sky, coming from the direction of Brentwood Bay. They were too big for birds, yet too small for aircraft, and there was a moment's shocked incomprehension before we recognized them for what they were. Then they wheeled over the Newspocket van with a bedlam of yells and revealed themselves as teenages of both sexes, unclothed, but painted a simple black semi-matte exterior latex. There were nine of them.

In the weeks following, we came to know them as the Crows. They flew overhead, circled, then settled all over the garry oak and the roof of our house.

They made no attempt to harass Gran or Gramps. Indeed, they seemed almost reverential in their attitude toward the old people.

It seemed that Gran had unlocked some kind of floodgate in the human unconscious, and people took to the air in increasing numbers. The distributors of antigravity belts became millionaires almost overnight, and the peninsula skies became a bright tapestry of wheeling, screeching figures in rainbow colours and startling nakedness.

The media named them the Byrds.

"I view it as a protest against today's moral code," Dr Pratt said. Now he spent most of his time on panels or giving interviews. "For more years than I care to remember, people have been repressed, their honest desires cloaked in conformity just as tightly as their bodies have been swathed in concealing garb. Now, suddenly, people are saying they've had enough. They're pleasing themselves. It shouldn't surprise us. It's healthy. It's good."

It was curious, the way the doctor had become pro-Byrd. These days he seemed to be acting in the capacity of press agent for Gran — who herself had become a cult figure. In addition he was working on his learned paper, "The Origins and Spread of Avian Tendencies in Humans".

Pandora and I reckoned he was in the pay of the belt people.

"But it's fun to be in the centre of things," she said one evening, as the Crows came in to roost, and the garry oak creaked under the weight of a flock of Glaucous Gulls come to pay homage to Gran. "It's put Sidney on the map — and your family too." She took my hand, smiling at me proudly.

There were the Pelicans, who specialized in high dives into Cordova Bay, deactivating their belts in midair, then reactivating them underwater to rocket Polaris-like from the depths. They rarely caught fish, though; and frequently had to be treated for an ailment known as Pelican's Balloon, caused by travelling through water at speed with an open mouth.

There were the Darwin's Tree Finches, a retiring sect whose existence went unsuspected for some weeks because they spent so much time in the depths of the forested Highlands area with cactus spines held between their teeth, trying to extract bugs from holes in dead trees. They were a brooding and introspective group.

Virtually every species of bird was represented. And because every cult must have its lunatic fringe, there were the Pigeons. They flocked to the streets of downtown Victoria and mingled with the crowds hurrying to and fro. From the shoulders up they looked much like anyone else, only greyer, and with a curious habit of jerking their heads while walking. Bodily, though, they were like any other Byrd: proudly unclothed.

Their roosting habits triggered the first open clash between Byrds and Man. There were complaints that they kept people awake at night, and fouled the rooftops. People began to string electrified wires around their ridges and guttering, and to put poison out.

The Pigeons' retaliation took place early one evening, when the home-going pedestrians jammed Douglas Street. It was simple and graphic, and well-coordinated. Afterward people referred to it obliquely as the Great Deluge, because it was not the kind of event which is discussed openly in proper society.

There were other sects, many of them; and perhaps the strangest was a group who eschewed the use of antigravity belts altogether. From time to time we would catch sight of them sitting on the rocks of Mount Douglas, searching one another for parasites. Their bodies were painted a uniform brown except for their private parts, which were a luminous red. They called themselves Hamadryas Baboons.

People thought they had missed the point of the whole thing, somehow.

Inevitably when there are large numbers of people involved, there are tragedies. Sometimes an elderly Byrd would succumb to cardiac arrest in midair and drift away on the winds. Others would suffer belt malfunctions and plummet to the ground. As the first chill nights began to grip the Saanich Peninsula, some of the older Byrds died of exposure and fell from their perches. Courageously they maintained their role until the end, and when daylight came they would be found in ritualistic "Dead Byrd" postures, on their backs with legs in the air.

"All good things come to an end," Dr Pratt said one evening as the russet leaves drifted from the trees. It had been a busy day, dozens of groups having come to pay homage to Gran. There was a sense of wrapping up, of things coming to a climax. "We will stage a mass rally," said Dr Pratt to the Newspocket reporter. "There will be such a gathering of Byrds as the country has never known. Gran will address the multitude at the Great Coming Down."

Mother said, "So long as it's soon. I don't think Gran can take any more of this weather."

I went to invite Pandora to the Great Coming Down, but she was not at home. I was about to return when I caught sight of a monstrous thing sitting on the backyard fence. It was bright green except around the eyes, which were grey, and the hair, which was a vivid yellow. It looked at me. It blinked in oddly reptilian fashion. It was Pandora.

She said, "Who's a pretty boy, then?"

The very next day Gran swooped down from the garry oak, seized Mother's scarf with her toes, and a grim tug of war ensued.

"Let go, you crazy old fool!" Mother shouted.

Gran cranked her belt up to maximum lift and took a quick twist of the scarf around her ankles. The other end was wrapped snugly around Mother's neck and tucked into her heavy winter coat. Mother left the ground, feet kicking. Her shouts degenerated into strangled grunts.

Father got a grip of Mother's knees as she passed overhead and Gran, with a harsh screech of frustration, found herself descending again, whereupon Gramps, having observed the scene with bright interest, came winging in and took hold of her, adding the power of his belt to hers.

Father's feet left the ground.

Mother by now had assumed the basic hanging attitude: arms dangling limply, head lolling, tongue protruding, face empurpled. I jumped and got hold of Father's ankles. There was a short, sharp rending sound and we fell back to earth in a heap, Mother on top. Gran and Gramps flew back to the garry oak with their half of the scarf, and began to eat it. Father pried the other half away from Mother's neck. She was still breathing.

"Most fascinating," Dr Pratt said.

"My wife nearly strangled by those goddamned brutes and he calls it fascinating?"

"No — look at the Hornbills."

"So they're eating the scarf. So they're crazy. What's new?"

"They're not eating it. If you will observe closely, you will see they are shredding it. And look — the female is working the strands around that clump of twigs. It's crystal clear what they're doing, of course. This is a classic example of nest building."

The effect on Father was instantaneous. He jumped up, seized Dr Pratt by the throat and, shaking him back and forth, shouted, "Any fool knows birds only nest in the spring!" He was overwrought, of course. He apologized the next day.

By that time the Byrds were nesting all over the peninsula. They used a variety of materials and in many instances their craftmanship was pretty to see. Victoria Newspocket ran a competition for "The Nest I Would Be Happiest To Join My Mate In", treating the matter as a great joke, although some of the inhabitants who had been forcibly undressed in the street thought otherwise. The Byrds wasted nothing. Their nests were intricately woven collections of whatever could be stolen from below: hats, overcoats, shirts, pants, clothesline, undergarments, hearing aids, wigs.

"The nesting phenomenon has a two-fold significance," Dr Pratt informed the media. "On the one hand, we have the desire of the Byrds to emulate the instinctive behavioural patterns of their avian counterparts. On the other hand, there is undoubtedly a suggestion of — how can I say it? — aggression towards the earthbound folk. The Byrds are saying, in their own way: join us. Be natural. Take your clothes off. Otherwise we'll do it for you."

"You don't think they're, uh, sexually *warped*?" the reporter asked.

"Sexually liberated," Dr Pratt insisted.

The Byrds proved his point the next day, when they began to copulate all over the sky.

It was the biggest sensation since the Great Deluge. Writhing figures filled the heavens and parents locked their children indoors and drew the drapes. It was a fine day for love; the sun glinted on sweat-bedewed flesh, and in the unseasonable warmth the still air rang with cries of delight. The Byrds looped and zoomed and chased one another, and when they met they coupled. Artificial barriers of species were cast aside and Eagle mated with Chaffinch, Robin with Albatross.

"Clearly a visual parable," said Dr Pratt. "The —"

"Shut up," said Mother. "Shut up, shut up, shut *up*!"

In the garry oak, Rufous-necked Hornbill mated with Rufous-necked Hornbill, then with Crow; then, rising joyously into the sky, with Skua, with Lark, and finally with Hamadryas Baboon, who had at last realized what it was all about and strapped on a belt.

"She's eighty years old! What is she thinking of?"

"She's an Earth Mother to them," Dr Pratt explained.

"Earth Mother my ass," Father said. "She's stark, staring mad, and it's about time we faced up to it."

"It's true, it's true!" wailed Mother, a broken woman. "She's crazy! She's been crazy for years! She's old and useless, and yet she keeps filling in all that stuff on her Peace form, instead of forgetting like any normal old woman!"

"Winter is coming," Dr Pratt said, "and we are witnessing the symbolic Preservation of the Species. Look at that nice young Tern up there. Tomorrow they must come back to earth, but in the wombs of the females the memory of this glorious September will live on!"

"She's senile and filthy! I've seen her eating roots from out of the ground, and do you know what she did to the Ever-attentive Waiter? She crosswired it with the Mailgift chute and filled the kitchen with self-adhesive cookies!"

"She did?" And the first shadow of doubt crossed Dr Pratt's face. The leader of the Byrds crazy?

"And one day a game show called on the visiphone and asked her a skill-testing question which would have set us all up for life — and she did the most disgusting thing, and it went out live and the whole of British Columbia saw it!"

"I'm sure she has sound psychological reasons for her behaviour," Dr Pratt said desperately.

"She doesn't! She's insane! She walks into Sidney rather than fill out a Busquest form! She brews wine in a horrible jar under the bed! She was once sentenced to one week's community service for indecent exposure! She trespasses in those fields around the airport, picking blackberries! You want to know why the house stinks? She programmed the Pesterminator to zap the Tidy Mice!"

"But I thought ... Why didn't you tell me before? My God, when I think of the things I've said to Victoria Newspocket! If this comes out, my reputation, all I've worked for, all ... " He was becoming incoherent. "Why didn't you tell me?" he asked again.

"Well, Jesus Christ, it's obvious, isn't it?" Father snapped. "Look at her. She's up in the sky mating with a Hamadryas Baboon, or something very much like one. Now that's what I call crazy."

"But it's a *movement* ... It's free and vibrant and so basic, so —"

"A nut cult," Father said firmly. "Started by a nut case and encouraged by a quack. Nothing more, nothing less. And the forecast for tonight is heavy frost. It'll wipe out fifty percent of them. You'd better get them all down, Pratt, or you'll have a few hundred deaths on your conscience."

But the Byrds came down of their own accord, later that day. As though sensing the end of the Indian summer and the chilly nights to come, they drifted out of the sky in groups, heading for earth, heading for us. Gran alighted in the garry oak with whirling arms, followed by Gramps. They sat close together on their accustomed branch, gobbling quietly to each other. More Byrds came; the Crows, the Pelicans. They filled the tree, spread along the ridge of the roof and squatted on the guttering. They began to perch on roofs, trees, fences and posts along Resthaven, all species intermingled. Soon they were all settled, a great final gathering of painted people who, just for a few weeks, had gone a little silly. They looked happy but tired, and a few were shivering as the afternoon shortened into evening. They made a great noise at first; a rustling and screeching and fluid piping, but after a while they quietened down. I saw Pandora amidst them, painted and pretty, but her gaze passed right through me. They were still Byrds, playing their role until the end.

And they all faced Gran.

They were awaiting the word to Come Down, but Gran remained silent, living every last moment. It was like standing in the centre of a vast amphitheatre, with all those heads turned toward us, all those beady eyes watching us. The Newspocket crew were nowhere to be seen; they probably couldn't get through the crowd.

Finally Dr Pratt strode forward. He was in the grip of a great despondency. He was going to come clean.

"Fools!" he shouted. A murmur of birdlike sounds arose, but soon died. "All through history there have been fools like you, and they've caused wars and disasters and misery. Fools without minds of their own, who follow their leader without thought, without stopping to ask if their leader knows what he is doing. Leaders like Genghis Khan, like Mussolini, like Hitler, leaders who manipulate their followers like puppets in pursuit of their own crazy ends. Crazy leaders drunk with power. Crazy leaders like Gran up there.

"Yes, Gran is crazy! I mean certifiably crazy, ready for Peace. Irrational and insane and a burden to the State and to herself. She had me fooled at first." He uttered a short, bitter laugh, not unlike the mating cry of Forster's Tern. "I thought I found logic in what she did, such was the cunning nature of her madness. It was only recently when I investigated Gran's past record, that I unmasked her for what she is: a mentally unbalanced old woman with marked antisocial tendencies. I could give you chapter and verse of Gran's past misdemeanours — and I can tell you right now, this isn't the first time she's taken her clothes off in public — but I will refrain out of consideration for her family, who have suffered enough.

"It will suffice to say that I have recommended her committal and the Peace Wagon is on its way. The whole affair is best forgotten. Now, come down out of those trees and scrub off, and go home to your families, all of you."

He turned away, shoulders drooping. It was nothing like the Great Coming Down he'd pictured. It was a slinking thing, a creeping home, an abashed admission of stupidity.

Except that the Byrds weren't coming down. They sat silently on their perches, awaiting the word from Gran.

All through Dr Pratt's oration she'd been quiet, staring fixedly at the sky. Now at last she looked around. Her eyes were bright but it was an almost-human brightness, a different thing from the beady stare of the past weeks. And she half-smiled through the paint, but she didn't utter a word.

She activated her belt and, flapping her arms, rose into the darkening sky.

And the Byrds rose after her. They filled the sky, a vast multitude of rising figures, and Pandora was with them. Gran led, Gramps close behind, and then came Coot and Skua and Hawk and the whole thousand-strong mob. They wheeled once over the town and filled the evening with a great and lonely cry. Then they headed off in V-formations, loose flocks, tight echelons, a pattern of dwindling dark forms against the pale duck-egg blue of nightfall.

"Where in hell are they all going?" shouted Dr Pratt as I emerged from the shed, naked and painted. It was cold, but I would soon get used to it.

"South," I said.

"Why the hell south? What's wrong with here, for God's sake?"

"It's warmer, south. We're migrating."

So I activated my belt and lifted into the air, and watched the house fall away below me, and the tiny bolts of light as the Pesterminator hunted things. The sky seemed empty now but there was still a pink glow to the west. Hurrying south over Puget Sound, I saw something winking ahead like a red star and, before long, I was homing in on the gleaming hindquarters of a Hamadryas Baboon.

GHOST HOUSE
Lorna Crozier

SIX years ago, I accepted a job that required me to move from Saskatoon, where I wanted to continue living. I broke the news to my friends and waited for their sympathy. I didn't get much when I went on to say that the job was in Victoria. I got even less from my new neighbours on Vancouver Island. When they asked where I was from and I answered "Saskatchewan" the common reply was "Aren't you lucky to be here!"

Well, yes, perhaps I am. Only a fool would want to go through the last two terrible winters on the prairies, but I'm a dyed-in-the-wool Saskatchewanian and the list of what I miss could stretch a straight mile down a country road. One of those things is the light: its bright, unblinking gaze is incomparable. Another is the snow: its soft, slow fall that muffles the world, its perfect stars melting on your tongue, the hard-edged shadows that slide long and blue across the drifts.

We had snow in Victoria this winter, the most this corner of the country has ever seen. For some of us, it was a small, nostalgic gift. The neighbourhoods came alive with children building forts, sledding down the slightest incline, and throwing snowballs. I wondered how they knew how to do those things. Is there a Canadian gene in all of us, even those born in Victoria, that gets activated by a fierce winter storm? These coastal kids were suddenly sporting toques and bright red mittens, as if some prairie grandmother had knit and purled through the night.

The sound of children playing in the snow took me immediately to where I go when I think of the word "home": an old, ramshackle two-storey in Swift Current, Saskatchewan. It could have been a gracious house, but by the time my mother and father moved in, it needed tough love. They didn't give it that; after all, they were only renters, paying fifty dollars a month, and the landlady refused to fix anything, even the furnace that regularly expired from overwork. Many winter mornings my brother and I ran downstairs from our bedrooms to shiver and dress in front of the cookstove.

In spite of its drawbacks, which were most obvious to my mother, I loved that house. Under the cracked linoleum, strips of oak showed through. I followed the swirl of their grain and knots with my fingers. A wooden sliding door, heavy on its track, separated the front hall from my parents' bedroom. The door became a secret passageway in my many hours of make-believe. The picture windows, made of leaded glass, splashed colour on the walls and floors when the afternoon sun broke through. If I put my arm in the right spot, it would glimmer red, blue and green, as if my skin had turned to scales. We lived in luxury. For one thing, the kids from the neighbourhood gathered at our house. They never had to tiptoe; they weren't told don't touch, don't spill, don't slide down the banister.

The yard was even more accommodating. Every other house on the street boasted flower beds, trimmed lawns and hedges. My parents tilled the soil for a potato patch and never owned a lawn mower. Our hedge was one huge poplar that scattered sticky seeds up and down the block. Almost every morning in spring, I held my dog in my lap and pulled them from the fur between her toes.

The yard was my father's territory. A displaced farmer who drove a backhoe for the city, his real calling was collecting junk. Oil drums, piles of long pipes he'd pilfered from a field, boards dangerous with nails, a rusted length of chain, an old tractor seat — all of these rose from a sea of crabgrass lush and waving in the wind.

In April, run-off from the street above us streamed down the alley and flooded what would be the garden one month later. A miniature slough, it was the perfect place to test last year's rubber boots and float a raft built from Dad's scrap lumber. In winter, my friends and I made a circle in the snow and played fox and goose, finding safety only if we ran down the radius, our scarves flying, and reached the centre we called home.

This house was the centre of the universe. It was the place I wanted to be. I thought my contentment would last forever, but one fall afternoon, a few months after my sixth birthday, it vanished. A girl whom I'd just met in grade one stopped with me after school at the top of the alley. She pointed to my house and said, "I wonder what poor people live there." I remember that moment as one sliced out of time, an instant of sad and profound insight. For the first time, I felt ashamed of where I came from. I said goodbye to her and walked past my house to the end of the block until I was sure she was gone, then I doubled back and picked my way through the junk in the yard to our door.

I never felt the same about the house. We lived in it for seven more years until even its rent was too much, Dad laid off for most of the winter from his oil patch job, Mom bringing home too little from doing housework and selling tickets at the swimming pool. We moved into a cramped, dilapidated duplex. That first house, however, has continued to play a significant role in my imaginings and in many of the choices I've made.

Just as the man I ended up with has many aspects of my father, so the four houses Patrick Lane and I have owned during our time together have been replicas of this one. They've all been two-storeys with a plain, honest front they put on for the world. They've all been old with sagging porches, dank basements and hardwood hidden under wall-to-wall. In every one, we've replaced the roof, the wires, the fence; we've scraped the wooden siding, broken our backs with repairing. When we've done all we can, and the house is truly beautiful, we move. Money is not our motivation; we've lost with every sale.

Only Patrick can explain his reasons for this bizarre behaviour, but I can't help but wonder if I'm repaying some kind of debt. Do I rescue these fallen dowagers because every time we sand, patch the leaks, strip the stained wallpaper, I'm reaching back through time and giving the old house in Swift Current the spruce-up it deserved? Am I making some kind of recompense for my young self's fickle adulation and shame?

We've lived in our present house, twenty minutes from Victoria, for five years, longer than in any of the others. Because we've almost finished the repairs, I can sense us getting itchy feet. We've asked a realtor to keep an eye out. Our place is an old farmhouse, two storeys of course, built in 1910 in what was then the middle of a strawberry field. We fell in love with it at first sight. The house from Swift Current was asserting itself again — this one had all the dereliction we desired.

After we moved in, I walked around for days crying like Goethe on his deathbed, "More light, more light!" Living up to the stereotype of people from Saskatchewan, we cut down trees, I admit it, but the yard was full of them, choking the sunlight. We tore ivy off the windows, removed torn awnings and blinds, and punched four skylights in the new roof, two for the small room that is my office. Between writing poems, I lean back in my chair and watch an old poplar going through the seasons. This winter there was even snow along its branches.

When the snow became more of a burden than a delight (remember, the average prairie farmer owns more snow-removing equipment than the City of Victoria), I felt guilty, as if my longing for that other place had brought it here. The poplar's bigger than the one in the corner of the yard in Swift Current, but it's probably younger. Some fall mornings the light is as dense in its leaves as I remember it, a thousand miles and more than forty years away. Maybe Patrick and I will stay here. We'll call the realtor and tell him we don't want to see that handyman's special waiting for us around the corner. Maybe after all these years we've done enough for me to put the ghost of my old family house finally to rest.

ANNA'S MEDICINE
Sylvia Olsen

IN the summer of 1969 we moved to Victoria. Freed from Winnipeg's snowdrifts, face-freezing wind, sweltering heat and mosquitoes. Released from the kind of boredom that sticks to your brain and makes you shut your windows and doors and turn up the heat or down the air conditioner.

It was Mom's condition that caused the move and the boredom, the closing down the shades and locking the doors. She kept us out of the cold and the possibility of something, anything happening. From the winter of 1966 she abandoned her assured resilient self and bit by bit removed herself and us from the outside world. Fun and curiosity that once drove Mom was replaced by fear. "Be careful" and "You never know what might happen" became our family's mantras. Especially when it came to Michael.

When Mom wasn't tending to Michael's health she sat on her rocker with the front panels of her cardigan stretched one on top of the other. Her arms would be firmly placed across her chest, each hand massaging the other arm. While she rocked Michael played with mounds of toys spread across the floor around her chair. She would say, "Yes." "Not so loud." "Careful." "Are you feeling okay, Michael?" For three years Mom had focused her attention on him. His asthma. She was sure he was going to die from it. Although she never said the word.

In Winnipeg I locked myself in my room with stacks of the old home-improvement and decorator magazines that Mom hadn't looked at for years, sketching fences, houses, sheds, skyscrapers. I stretched walls out of proportion, ballooned windows, obscured porches and doorways with deformed trees and hedges, elongated roofs like pull taffy and bent chimneys like wilted flowers. I had grown accustomed to sitting behind the safety of my bedroom door and creating my own world with my sketch pad and pencils. But there were days when I was so bored I thought my head was going to blow up like the fireworks on the first of July. Other days I thought it would dissolve into a puddle of jelly.

You can't blame Winnipeg for what Mom was going through. But it didn't help. It wasn't the sort of place where you got out and about. At least our family didn't. So in the spring when Dad announced he had a new job and we were moving I was thrilled. He brought home travel brochures that showed the Empress Hotel and Butchart Gardens, the beaches of East Sooke Park. They talked about flowers, green lawns and lush landscapes. I studied the pictures and drew warped images of the Oak Bay Beach Hotel and Parliament Buildings.

We arrived in Victoria in July and Dad went to work at his new job at the University of Victoria history department. We moved into a white stucco bungalow in Cadboro Bay with black shutters and a sprawling lawn neatly bordered by flowering shrubs and red-leafed maples. Dad figured the garden would do Mom good. "She can get out in the fresh air," he said.

His plan to bring Mom to the West Coast to help her get "out of her shell" got off to a good start. The first few mornings she opened the curtains and gasped, "It's so green, so lovely." By the fall and the first rain Mom started to see the lush landscape as a threat. "Everything's *so damp*." When she said the word *damp* you wanted to dry yourself off.

Soon Mom began to prepare for Michael's asthma attacks.

She scheduled doctors' appointments, dusted the house and bundled him in a down jacket, hat and mittens whenever he went outside. She stayed focused on Michael but after the move she lost track of me. She no longer demanded that I come home directly after school. When I asked if I could go for a walk after supper she said yes.

The door was open and I was out in a world I didn't know existed. My new world included posters in the school hall advertising protests against the Viet Nam war and the threat of nuclear bombs. There were boys with long hair and girls with hipster cord pants and embroidered unbleached cotton Mexican blouses. Kids smoked Export As and talked about rolling your own and hash pipes and roaches. I ran the pointed end of the comb down the centre of my head and parted my hair exactly. I bought white lipstick and a pair of moccasins. I hung a poster in my bedroom that had a picture of a dead beat looking Indian like the ones I had seen in Winnipeg. The caption read, "Walk a mile in my moccasins."

"Those slippers have any soles?"Dad asked one drizzly afternoon.

"Not really."

I made friends with two sisters who lived up the street. Kara and Karrissa. They bleached their hair white-blond and wore four-inch hoop earrings. They bought leather and made vests with beaded tassels front and back that swung freely past their hips. They wore knee-high mukluks and miniskirts so short they walked with their knees pressed together. They had beaded headbands and talked about Native spirituality. On their wall was a poster with a picture of Chief Seattle leaning on a cane. He said, "Every part of this country is sacred to my people."

When I went over to Kara and Karrissa's house they played Bob Dylan. We read passages from *The Prophet*. They closed their eyes and lowered their voices when they quoted the old Indian chief as if they were praying to a sacred god. "Men come and go like waves ..." or "A few more moons, a few more winters, and not one of all the mighty hosts that once filled this broad land will remain to weep over the tombs of my people."

I had never thought of Indians as spiritual. Mom had grabbed my arm and pulled me close to her whenever we passed Indians in Winnipeg. Groups of scrubby men and women, dogs and children sat on the streets, sometimes with hats opened up at their feet. I wanted to drop them a dime or nickel but Mom made sure we never got close enough. If an Indian staggered toward us Mom tightened her grasp around our hands and sped up.

She'd spit through her teeth. "The streets aren't safe anymore." "Why don't they go back to the reserve where they belong?"

I liked wearing moccasins and reading the old chief. I made a headband and slipped it over my straightened hair as soon as I said goodbye to Dad in the mornings. When Kara, Karrissa and I went to town after school I made sure to place a dime in the hand of any Indian who was begging on the street corner. I liked the feel of their rough skin.

If I stayed over for supper at Kara and Karrissa's house we had lively discussions with their parents about women's roles and civil disobedience. Their dad was a lawyer. He defended draft dodgers and worked on cases dealing with human rights. Cases, he said, "That would have tugged the short and curlies of my father and grandfather." Apparently they were lawyers before him.

Conversations at our supper table were dull and predictable. Mom read the newspaper in the morning and reported the news to us at night. "Did you know the mayor went to San Francisco?" "The owner of the supermarket got a parking ticket." Mom listed names of people who were marrying or travelling. We chewed on pork or pot roast while Mom listed bargains at Oakcrest and Wellburns. She informed us of any change in the price of toilet paper and Miracle Whip.

Most conversations ended or started with something about the cold. *Damp* cold. What was she going to do with Michael? I got tired of Mom's conversations and concentrated mainly on the sound behind my ears of grinding meat.

There's plenty of rain in Victoria. Wet from the time you wake up until you go to bed. It had been like that for the first three weeks of November and Mom had been anxiously anticipating Michael's next asthma attack. She had fallen back into the old habit she had in Winnipeg of rocking back and forth waiting for something to go wrong. Dad was getting pretty discouraged and I ignored her as long as she let me go out with my friends. But Mom did something that November that started things changing around our house.

It was a Saturday morning.

I'm setting the syrup and sliced oranges on the table. Dad's reading the newspaper and Michael's waiting for Mom to serve pancakes.

Mom says, "I'm going to go out to the Indian reserve to buy Michael an Indian sweater." Her voice is solid, like she's said things like that before.

The comment is enough out of the ordinary that Dad raises his head and says, "What?"

"I'm going to go out to the Indian reserve to buy Michael an Indian sweater."

It was the Indian part that took me by surprise. Mom's in the habit of buying Michael sweaters, coats, mittens, hats. They're her protection from the fear of losing him. Cold is the enemy. Mom is a warrior. Buying armour is nothing new. But it's the first time I've ever heard her say Indian not *Indian*, making a face like she's bitten into a lemon.

"What's an Indian sweater?" I ask.

"I read about them in an article. It's there in the second section."

Dad looks annoyed when Mom rummages through the paper until she finds the page.

"It says Indian sweaters are the best protection from the damp West Coast weather. Indian women have been making them for years. There's something in the wool that keeps the cold out."

Dad brushes the article aside and searches for the section he was reading.

"I'm going out this afternoon. A sweater's just what Michael needs."

Dad says, "You're going where this afternoon?"

"It's only twenty minutes out the highway. On the Saanich Peninsula. We can find it on the map."

"Lyla. You can buy those sweaters downtown. Just take the bus." Dad says it like Mom couldn't have thought of it herself.

"But the article says when you buy a sweater directly from the reserve the knitter measures you up and you know you've got a good one. And it's cheaper too."

Dad perks up at the mention of the word cheaper.

I'm shocked Mom even thinks about driving to an Indian reserve for any reason. But Michael's asthma is her biggest fear and prevention's about the only thing that will get her out of the house.

"The article quotes a woman saying she was sick since the day her family moved from the prairies to Victoria until she bought an Indian sweater." Mom pulls out a map and carries on, "It's got to be here in Brentwood. It says IR. That must mean Indian reserve."

Dad says, "What's the address?"

"The Tarslip Indian Reserve. The knitter's name is Anna." Mom skims over the article. "No address."

"You can't go without an address. And what about her last name?"

Dad leaves for the university convinced it's settled. No address, no last name, no Indian sweater. He has a way of making those sorts of thing plain. Go to town. Buy an Indian sweater from a perfectly decent store. For Dad it makes sense. Same knitters. Same sweaters. For Mom things aren't in straight lines like that. If the article says the woman bought the sweater directly from a knitter and then she never gets sick how is Mom to know it isn't because she drove out to the reserve and had the knitter measure her up. Mom's precise about details when it comes to Michael's health.

I want to drive out to the Indian reserve. I imagine old men with squinty eyes sitting outside large wooden houses smoking long pipes as they contemplate solitude and eagles and other important things. The reserve will be a dignified place where Indians live like Indians. Although I doubt they'll be wearing beaded headbands or tasselled leather vests.

"Lisa, you're coming with us." Mom says. She enters the kitchen purse in hand after Dad shuts the door. "Get Michael."

"How are we going to find the knitter without a last name or an address?"

"We'll look for sweaters hanging on clotheslines. That's how passers-by know the knitter has something to sell."

Mom's face is bright in a way I've seldom seen lately.

"I've borrowed money from the grocery tin."

We drive north on the Pat Bay Highway. The map is spread on the front seat between Mom and me. She drives silently, both hands on the steering wheel. I feel uneasy. Her need for concentration worries me. She can tolerate no distractions. There's always the possibility of some unstated disaster.

Michael darts from side to side in the back seat looking at fields, cows, horses, trees, the Haro Strait and Mount Baker. When Michael exclaims, "Look!" Mom replies with a sharp "Shush!"

We turn left on Keating Cross Road.

I keep my eyes peeled for any sign of Indians, a tepee, a tent. We pass rolling fields but nothing that looks like Indians. At first I was feeling excited but now I'm more queasy than anything. I'm feeling a little worried that Mom might not have this plan together.

We reach Brentwood Bay and pull into a grocery store parking lot on West Saanich Road.

"Go in and ask them where the Tarslip Indian Reserve is."

I can tell from the spelling that Mom's been pronouncing the name wrong. But when I try to sound *Tsartlip* in my head I don't sound any better.

"And ask them if they know a woman named Anna who lives there."

"Oh, do you know Laura? She comes from Winnipeg." Kids at school ask me stupid questions like that. "Winnipeg's a big place," I say. "Thousands of people live there, maybe hundreds named Laura."

I don't move.

Mom's beginning to lose sight of the sweater and Michael and his asthma. I can see her mind is flitting between her fears and her need to protect him. Her eyes float in pools. "Please, Lisa," she says.

"They're Chinese in that place," I say when I return to the car. "They didn't understand what I was saying. But the guy pointed that way first and then that way. So I think we should head back up West Saanich Road and then turn down ..." My eyes follow my finger on the map. "Turn down Stelly's Cross Road and that's the reserve."

"And then where?" At this point Mom needs exactness.

"We'll decide when we get there."

"Lisa," her voice quivers.

"Mom start the car. We'll be okay. I'll ask when we get there."

We turn down Stelly's Cross Road and I watch for signs of Indians. On the right side of the road — the reserve from what the map says — there are fields of long grass, an old barn and a few small wooden houses. On the other side — not the reserve — it isn't much different. At the bottom of the hill we see a small chipped and peeled sign that reads Tsartlip Indian Reserve. Private Property. Keep Out. Not something Mom or I expect.

Mom pulls the station wagon onto the gravel shoulder. Her hands are shaking and I can see she's not going to hold it together much longer if I don't do something.

"Lisa."

An old man shuffles toward us from the other side of the

sign. I open the door, slide out of the car and approach him. He's small and bent. Scruffs of white hair poke out from underneath his battered red cap. A white shirt is tucked neatly into his pants, which hang loose from wide black suspenders. The long end of a twisted tie falls past his hips. His baggy plaid jacket looks like a hand-me-down from a professor at the university.

I clear my throat to get his attention but he doesn't hesitate. "Hello."

His steps slow down until he leans back on his heels and turns his neck.

"Hello." I say again.

He nods.

"I'm looking for Anna."

He nods again.

I wait.

"Why you looking for her?"

"We've come to buy an Indian sweater."

While the old man looks at me I'm struggling to find a voice that fits. I think about Chief Seattle's words and Kara and Karrissa's demure accent when they quote him. But that doesn't seem right for this occasion.

"We want a sweater for my little brother." My own voice seems to work just fine.

He opens his lips in a wide grin exposing a mouth of scattered teeth. Then he turns and begins to retrace his steps motioning me over his shoulder. I walk closely behind him and wave my hand so Mom will follow. We pass a tiny wooden shack no bigger than a garage. The blankets tacked to the windows make me think it's a house but I'm not sure. Up ahead there's a young guy with an axe and muscles bulging out from under his short sleeves. With one swing he splinters a huge block of wood into a dozen pieces then tosses them onto a pile.

"Hey Charlie," he calls as our procession passes his woodpile. "Got visitors?"

"Hey son," the old man keeps walking. "Anna does."

The young guy looks right at me. He smiles. I want to stop and sit on the pile of wood. I'm pretty sure from the look in his eyes that he wants me to stop as well. But the old man continues walking so I keep going.

When we reach a driveway leading to two small shacks he says, "This is Anna's place."

"Thank you," I say. "That was kind of you."

The old man stands on the side of the driveway until Mom pulls the car off the road. Then he nods to us and heads back.

"Lisa ..." Mom shoots a worried glance around the property. Trampled long grass is covered by balls and bikes and tires and pots. Mounds of blackberry bushes crowd around the shacks. A line is strung between the two buildings with two massive sweaters hanging next to a least a dozen socks pegged one next to the other. As we near the front door the yard fills with kids. They back up toward the shack without taking their eyes off us or saying a word. I'm starting to feel like an intruder, like they caught me in the act of something criminal. I want to say, Hey kids, it's okay we haven't done anything wrong. We aren't going to hurt you. But they don't look afraid. They look more like they want to poke their fingers into our skin.

"I'm coming," a woman's voice comes through an open window.

Mom sidles up behind me and tugs on my jacket. Not to get my attention but to hold herself up. I can tell that this expedition on behalf of Michael's asthma has gone too far. I hold onto her elbow and feel her limp figure behind me.

A small, dark, round woman appears on the stair. Her hair is tied in a kerchief that makes her look like Aunt Jemima on the pancake syrup jar. She's wearing a long heavy brown skirt with a green cardigan buttoned under her chin. Her clumpy black boots are topped with men's work socks. Her face is smooth and olive-coloured. I figure she's younger than Mom by a few years. Her face hasn't begun to pull. There are no lines around her mouth or eyes.

"Hi, I'm Anna."

Some people stand so solidly on their feet that they give you the confidence to stand on yours even if you feel like turning and running away. Anna's like that. I relax and I can feel Mom relax too.

"I'm Lisa. This is Lyla, my mom. And this is Michael," I say. Mom tugs again when Michael bolts out of the car and heads directly to the group of kids that are now spread out across the yard.

"Michael," Mom's voice is barely more than a whisper. "Lisa, get Michael."

"Oh, that's okay. He can play with the kids," Anna says.

"We're here for an Indian sweater," I say. "Mom read about them in the newspaper."

Anna lets out a belly laugh and says. "Oh that."

She turns to go back into the house. "Come on in. Sorry it's so small. But at least you can sit down."

"Lisa, get Michael."

"I'll get us tea," Anna says. "Or do you want coffee?"

"Lisa!" Mom crackles. I've heard Mom sound like it before and it usually comes right before a blow-up or meltdown. Normally once she gets to this state of freaking out she either collapses quietly or screams until she does.

"Mom," I match her fear with firmness. "Leave him alone. Do you want tea or coffee?"

In the house Anna's pouring hot water into a large tin teapot. When Mom enters the room Anna places her hand on Mom's shoulder and speaks closely to Mom's face without looking at her.

"You want a sweater for your little boy?" she asks.

Mom's head bobs loosely in affirmation.

"Lisa? Is that your name?" Anna asks me.

"Yes."

"When you've finished your tea would you get your brother? I'll need to measure him up."

I take a few sips then leave the room and stand on the porch. There's not much to see other than bushes and a few shacks placed back off the narrow road. Over the hill tucked in behind a grove of giant maples by the beach is a wooden roof the size of a school gym. I can only see one corner of it but it looks like it might be an Indian longhouse like I've seen in pictures.

I hear Michael's voice, "Kick it over here!" So I walk in the direction of a group of boys kicking a ball between two stacks of tires. I pull him back to the house and reach the kitchen door in time to hear Mom say, "It's his asthma. And I'm worried day and night."

"Children are such a worry," Anna says. "I've lost so many I have to hold on tightly to the ones I have."

I gulp and hold Michael back so I can listen.

"What do you mean?" Mom asks. She sounds calm like she did years ago in Winnipeg when Maggie came to visit. They used to talk for hours and drink coffee and say stuff like, "Really? When did that happen? You've got to be kidding. You too?"

Anna says, "I gave birth to six children. Only three are still alive."

There's no sound.

"Two died at birth and one died of pneumonia when she was three."

I plan my next action. How can I pick Mom up off the floor and drag her to the car. How can I calm her down so she can drive us home?

Neither woman speaks.

Finally Anna breaks the silence. "What did you say your little boy had? Asthma?"

Mom must have nodded.

"I've just the thing for you," Anna says. I hear the sound of things bumping together in a cupboard. "Mix this with water and spread it on his chest when he's congested. The old lady Camellia up the street makes it."

Michael and I pause at the doorway as Mom tucks a metal jar

into her purse. She looks bewildered like her tongue is stuck behind her teeth. But there's no sign of panic and there doesn't seem to be any threat that she's going to go completely berserk.

"Did you say you needed to measure Michael for a sweater?" I say.

Anna wraps a tape around his chest then stretches it down his arm and back. Mom sips her tea. I wait for signs. Anna is too close to Mom's wounds for us to escape something dramatic. The last time someone talked about losing a child Mom fainted and Dad had to scoop her up and carry her out of the room.

Mom smiled when Michael chose a dancing deer from Anna's design book.

"More tea?" Anna asks.

Mom shakes her head.

"Next week then?"

"Will the sweater be ready in a week?" I ask. "That soon?"

"Oh, it'll be ready Monday," Anna says. "But your mom said you're coming out next Saturday."

"Wow. How come so fast?" I'm amazed. That day a lot of things had surprised me, but how could someone knit an entire sweater, even a little one, in two days?

"I'll have three sweaters finished by Saturday," Anna says. There's a matter-of-fact pride in her voice. "If you don't knit you don't eat. That's the rule around here."

She places her hand again on Mom's shoulder. "Thanks for coming. I enjoyed meeting you and your children."

Mom doesn't say anything, but other than that there isn't anything particularly strange about her.

Michael jumps in the back of the car. Mom nods and crawls in behind the wheel and I thank Anna and wave at the kids.

"Next week." I say.

"Next week."

I look for the guy with the axe when we pass the woodpile. He's gone. Maybe next Saturday. Maybe he chops wood every Saturday.

We drive back through the rolling fields of the Saanich Peninsula. Mom hums under her breath. Michael talks to himself. I think about what I will tell Kara and Karrissa. I think about the guy with the axe, his smile, his smooth skin and muscles.

When we get home no one says anything to Dad about the trip to the peninsula. Mom places the metal jar next to Michael's pills in the medicine cabinet and puts the grocery money back in the tin. She opens the drapes each morning before we leave for school and combs her hair.

One week later we're ready early. Saturday morning Mom drives directly to Stelly's Cross Road. She slows down only slightly when we pass the Private Property No Trespassing sign. My thighs and belly tingle when I see the guy and two others standing next to the woodpile. Their eyes follow our car as we slowly drive past them. I sit frozen like a wax figure in a parade. I want to yell at Mom to speed up. At the same time I want to tell her to stop so I can say to the guy, Hi, I'm Lisa. What's your name? He smiles and I press my hands against my stomach to stop it from vibrating.

"I hope you're hungry." Anna set tea and chunks of bread on the table and almost forgets the blackberry jam, adding, "It's fresh fried bread."

After they decide that Michael's sweater fits perfectly he disappears with a piece of bread dripping with jam. I follow him out the door to see if I can get a glimpse of the guy but we're too far away. I stand back near the door and listen to Mom and Anna.

"Did you use the medicine?"

"No, Michael was fine this week. I'm saving it."

"I had a sick boy myself this week. The medicine worked wonders."

"Do you have medicine for other ailments too?"

"Yes, but not for everything. That's why I lost my little girl to pneumonia. There was nothing I could do."

"How long ago was that?"

"Two years this January."

It's silent.

"You?"

"Me, what?"

"Have you lost a child?"

Mom must have nodded.

Anna says, "I thought so."

I can hear the sound of pouring.

"Here drink this."

"Thanks."

"How long ago?"

"Four years ago this January. The sixteenth. My son."

"It was the tenth when my little girl died. Linda. Her name was Linda."

"Robert."

I haven't heard my brother's name since his funeral.

Mom says, "You seem so strong."

"I have to be. For the other children. If I'm overcome by death and mourning for one child I'll take life from the others."

Suddenly I feel like I'm eavesdropping on a conversation that belongs to Mom. So I walk to the end of the driveway and peer down the road. I still can't see the guy with the axe.

When I return to the house Anna's measuring Mom's chest and arms and back.

"Next week?" Mom asks.

"Unless you come back earlier." Anna laughs and says, "I'll have it done for you Monday."

"We'll wait until Saturday. Maybe then we'll get one for Lisa too."

"Are you kidding Mom?"

We bring Kara and Karrissa out to Anna's the next week. Mostly they're looking for the guys by the woodpile but they're not there.

By the time we're finished even Dad has an Indian sweater.

Looking back I can see that the story Mom read in the newspaper was right. Our sweaters protected us from the damp cold West Coast air. And a lot of other things happened on that journey out to Tsartlip as well. I still wear my old sweater even after more than thirty years. Mom and Anna keep in touch. The metal jar sits in Mom's medicine cabinet unopened. Michael's fine. His asthma gave way to perfect health. Dad's sure that moving to Victoria was just the thing Mom needed to "get her out of her shell". I look closely and wonder whenever I see a broad-shouldered, olive-skinned Indian man with a friendly inviting white smile. What would have happened if I had stopped and said, "Hi, my name's Lisa. What's yours?"

SKIDNEY
MAC Farrant

NANA, my mother-in-law who lives with us, plays bridge Wednesday nights at the Sidney Silver Threads. She's usually home by ten but this week she came through the door at eight forty-five. Came into our bedroom, flushed and excited, and announced, "They evacuated the Centre! Gas leak!"

This was better than any disaster show on TV.

"There were sixteen tables of bridge," she told us, "and suddenly we could smell gas. Howard, the Director, called the Fire Department and then asked the players: 'You can either carry on with the bridge game or you can go home. What do you want to do?' And everyone yelled in one voice, 'Play Bridge.'"

When I heard this I immediately wrote the National Enquirer headline: *Seniors Elect To Play Bridge In Death Trap.*

And why wouldn't they? When you're seventy, or eighty, or ninety, why not play bridge in the midst of a potential explosion? It makes sense: it's a literal chance to go out with a bang. Possibly the last chance. And it's the opposite of those sad people who quit smoking a week before they die of lung cancer or who abandon their daily ration of cinnamon buns and take up weight training at age eighty-eight.

But the bridge players' thrill had been short-lived. A fireman dressed in a yellow-and-black rubber suit, a yellow helmet, and with an oxygen tank strapped to his back stood at the doorway to the bridge room and bellowed, "Evacuate! Now!"

"It was so exciting," Nana said. "Outside there were fire trucks and police cars with their lights flashing. And the road on either side of the Centre was closed off with that yellow tape you see on the news. What they use when there's a murder."

This is about as exciting as Sidney gets.

True, there's the Sidney Days Parade on July 1st followed by the giant sidewalk sale down Beacon Avenue. And there's the Santa Claus Parade where local businessmen attach helium-filled balloons to their mini-vans and holler at the shivering crowd, "Ten percent off blinds at Fashion Focus Paint & Accessories!"

But exciting?

This year the Santa Claus parade included our son Leslie's band playing live music from the back of a flatbed truck. They had seven blocks in which to impress the crowd. When they passed by us, the band was in the pause between songs. What we got was some amp noise. Seven blocks goes by fast even at the pace of a parade. My husband, Gerry, only got one blurred picture of our son's back while he was tuning his guitar.

The band's other guitarist took thirty minutes off work at The Pantry, where he's a short order cook, so he could be in the parade. How small town, I thought. I pictured him throwing off his greasy apron and running out of the restaurant at the last moment. Climbing onto the back of the truck as it began the parade and hastily donning his denim rock-star hat and carefully ripped jacket for his instant identity change.

It's like the Volunteer Fire Department. The man who's filling your tank at the gas station could, moments after the alarm sounds, be the same man hanging off the back of a wailing fire truck.

Sidney really is a small town — a small town on a largish island.

The main street, Beacon Avenue, veers off the Pat Bay Highway, a four-lane road whose main purpose is to link Victoria with the ferry terminal to the mainland. Day and night, cars scream past Sidney trying to make the ferry a couple of miles down the road. You can picture the panicked ferry-goers clawing at their car windows. "A cute island, yes, but let us off RIGHT NOW!!"

Take a breath, you want to call, there'll be ferry line-ups, delays, and what's so great about Vancouver? This is much the same message Sidney's town officials have tried to convey. Hoping to share in the tourist money that Victoria attracts, they've spiffed the place up with paving-stone sidewalks and nautical-style street signs. A billboard on the highway before you reach the town announces hopefully: Welcome to Beautiful Sidney by the Sea.

Those of us who live in or around Sidney agree it's a beautiful place. But many of us are glad the tourists largely ignore the town — we like it quiet and dull — and wish the officials would cease their relentless advertising campaigns. It's embarrassing. It's pathetic. It's like the time when I was ten years old and traveling in Oregon State with my family. Driving through a small town, we passed a run-down motel. A woman wearing an apron and a girl about my age rushed out from the motel and stopped our car. They looked desperate. "Please," the woman said, "stay here! We'll give you a really good rate."

My father couldn't drive away fast enough.

Sidney's town officials are trying to make Sidney into a travel destination. But you wonder if there really are excited families in Montana or Manitoba or Japan or New York planning a dream vacation to Sidney. This is just not a place you save up and travel to. Maybe, if the weather's good, you stop in for an hour or two on your way from Victoria to the ferry, poke around the nautical theme shops and Tanners Books and maybe take a stroll along the newly invented Port Sidney to look at the boats. But you won't stay here for long. Where's the theme park? Where's the mall?

Where's the world's largest stuffed salmon?

Our kids' name for Sidney is Skidney. A place light years away from the town inhabited by the handful of writers, the penny-conscious seniors, the young families in their starter homes. When I hear the word Skidney I naturally think of Skid Row, a despairing place filled with drunks, addicts and the homeless. But what the kids mean by Skidney is that it's a rough, down home, beer-drinking, unpretentious place. Skidney is a state of mind.

"In Skidney, when you go to a party, " a neighbourhood teenager told me, "you hold onto your beer. Actually hold onto it. There's all these kids standing around talking or they're dancing and they'll have cases of beer stuck under their arms. No one's crazy enough to put them down because they'll get taken. So the thing is, you hold onto them no matter what. A lot of girls wear packs and put their beer in there. People at Skidney parties are always coming up to you and trying to bum a beer. You look in your case and say, 'Hey man, I've only got eight left. Sorry.' If you put your beer down even for a minute, it's gone. That's Skidney."

Our daughter, Gabby, offers her version of Skidney:
      "There was this hard-core Barbie chick and she's like in the bowling alley with Mike Panowski. And she's supposedly his new girlfriend from Victoria? And I couldn't believe it. She thinks I'm hot on Mike because we're talking and it's weird how every time it's my turn to bowl it's his turn too. But I mean, like, Mike? Duh. But this Barbie chick keeps staring at me. Like a serious, big-time, jealousy trip. She's got these platform shoes on and tight black pants and perfect, wispy little bits of blonde hair pulled out of her ponytail. And she finally says to Mike before they've even finished their game, 'C'mon Mike, like, we're leaving.' And then she comes over to our table, all fake smiles and puts this half pitcher of beer in front of me and says, 'Like here, you can

have this.' And we're like, wow thanks, that's really cool! And it took Charlotte and me half an hour to figure it out. We were supposed to be insulted. Like in the Barbie chick's world this was an insulting thing to do. And it was such a laugh. Because in our world, in Skidney, this is the coolest thing you can do. Hey, you want to give us some free beer? Right on!"

I grew up in Cordova Bay, some ten miles down the road from Sidney. A place our kids refer to as "preppy".

"Kids in Cordova Bay blow dry their hair and wear Fashions," Leslie tells me disgustedly. "And they don't drink beer. At parties everyone puts their wine on the kitchen counter like grownups. When kids from Skidney go to one of their parties? The wine's gone in seconds."

When I was a brawling young person, my friends and I often went "slumming" at the Sidney Hotel. We'd drink beer and watch the fights in the "Beer Parlor", a large, noisy, brightly-lit, smoky room filled with small round tables covered in red terrycloth. Each table had as many glasses of beer as it could hold — twenty or thirty glasses — and beer cost twenty-five cents a glass. Around eleven or twelve in the evening there'd always be a drunken fight or two, and the police would come. My Cordova Bay friends and I imagined we were seeing the wild side of life, and it was thrilling.

"That's nothing," Gabby said when she heard this story. "A couple of fights? Like, how protected!"

Last Halloween Gerry drove seven costumed girls to a party up the road. The girls weren't actually invited but it was "cool" because they knew someone who knew someone who was having the party. It was an outdoors party and you had to wear a costume.

Seven girls piled into the back of our pick-up: a clown, a spider, a hooker, a Hawaiian in a pink wig, a New Age guru in a blue wig and white gown, a nymph wearing a crown of leaves, and a Raggedy Ann. Their packs bulged with cans of beer.

As they were pulling out of the driveway, one of the girls yelled to my husband, "Do you mind if I light this?"

Gerry, glancing in the rear view mirror, saw what he thought was a monster joint. "Yes!" he croaked, sweat forming on his upper lip. It turned out to be a Roman candle.

"Lighting *that* would have been even worse," he said when he returned home. He also said, "I can't believe I did that. Driving seven minors in possession of alcohol in the back of my truck. Thank Christ the police were busy searching delinquents for dope at the community bonfire."

"You go to a Skidney party," Leslie tells us, "and by ten o'clock most everyone's drunk and puking, drunk and screaming, or passed out."

"Sounds like the good old days to me," Gerry said.

For a year or two before I met him, Gerry was a regular at the Sidney Hotel. There are guys he drank with then who are still hanging around the local bars on a full-time basis. Guys who never went anywhere. In their forties and fifties now, they're either on welfare or working part-time in construction. If it's summer, maybe stripping boats at one of the local marinas. Their backs are gone, their knees are gone and if they ever had them, so are their families. The thing is, *they never got out of Sidney.*

Never getting out of Sidney is something our kids fear. What I hope they mean by this is: never getting beyond being what they call "a boozing loser".

We stayed in Sidney, Gerry and me, so in a sense we never got out, either. But then we moved on, I tell the kids, *in other ways.* "It doesn't matter where you live. What matters is how you look at things, how you *experience* your lives."

They get quiet when I talk like this. They don't want to think ten years down the road. They want to think: *tomorrow.* And maybe the day after that — Friday night! They want to believe right now will last forever.

And what I believe is: What else is there to do with youth but spend it fast?

We live in the Deep Cove area of Sidney. There's a small beach at the foot of our hill where, in summer, Gerry and I swim with our dog Mutz in the late afternoons. When the kids were small, before "Skidney" ever existed for us, they swam there, too. Those were years of riding on logs in the water and building castles on the sand bar, of seaweed fights and water skiing behind a neighbour's boat. And running up the hill late for supper, their beautiful suntanned bodies covered in fine, gray sand. Then flinging their inner tubes, their masks and snorkels, their wet towels onto the deck. Hosing themselves off before racing inside.

Now there's a new generation of young kids doing the same thing. And everyone down at the beach knows all the connections: whose kid belongs to who and where, exactly, they live. And isn't it great, everyone says, that Kira's grandmother at eighty-two still swims every day?

The main topic of conversation amongst the swimmers has never changed: water temperature. "How's the water today?" you might ask someone who's just towelling off. What you'll hear is anything from "Beautiful!" to "Freezing. It'll make your bones ache."

Over the years, we've learned to tell the temperature of the water just by looking at it. Clear means cold; cloudy means warm. And the warmest water is when it has a greenish-brown tinge to it, an algae bloom. We're always telling dubious newcomers, "No, that's *not* pollution. It's a red tide. The swimming will be great!"

More than once, Stan, a wiry senior citizen who lives in a waterfront house, has bounded down the beach when he sees us taking our shoes off and arranging our towels on the sand. When he makes such a determined visit, we know what he's going to say. "Hey there, folks," he'll call a good fifty feet before he reaches us, " did you hear that teenage party down here last night?"

"No!" we'll say, acting shocked by the very idea. We know

he suspects our kids. But we want him to think they spend every waking moment volunteering at the hospital or attending Bible camp or walking the dogs of invalids.

Once, he'd asked about another party. "It was coming from up your way," he said, jerking his head in the direction of our house. "The music was so loud. All we could hear was this thumping sound. Thump. Thump. Thump."

"Must have been my mother," Gerry had said brazenly. "She had a few of the ladies in for bridge last night. Must have put on Frank Sinatra. She's eighty-one but you know how these old girls like to have fun!"

"Hah! Eighty-one you say? Golly!"

It was, of course, *our* party and fourteen of our friends ripping up the carpet to the House sounds of Matthew Herbert Herbert and Bob Sinclair.

About the teenage beach party, Stan pressed on. "You didn't hear it?" he asked, incredulous. "That surprises me. The music was so *loud*. And there was yelling and girls in the water screaming. You didn't hear it up your place?"

"We must have slept through it," Gerry said, bored and picking up a stick for the dog. The dog, excited, turning in circles across the sand to the water.

"Gosh, it was loud," Stan continued. "I would have thought you'd hear it at your house. No? I was down here this morning picking up empty beer bottles. Some of them broken. The garbage they left! I picked up half a dozen empty chip bags and cigarette packs. "

"Wasn't that good of you?" I said and my husband shot me a glance.

"Yes, well. At ten-thirty I called the RCMP. Can you believe this? They couldn't come because of a house party in Sidney. Got out of control."

After Stan left to fling himself in the water and float on his back, Gerry, pretending not to talk to me, stared at the water and whispered out the side of his mouth, "Where were they last night?"

"At a house party in Sidney," I replied, gazing placidly at the tiny wind surfers in the distance. Then added, "But not at the rowdy one. Another one."

Gerry sighed. "So it wasn't *them* down here."

"No."

"I'm getting tired of Stan," my husband said.

That day we went for our usual swim. Gently parting the seaweed as we breast stroked along the shore, the dog beside us, the water was "Fantastic!" "Beautiful!" "Like soup!" A few swimmers on the beach were stretched out on their towels, drying off in the sun. Toddlers and their older brothers and sisters played with plastic boats at the water's edge.

While over in Skidney our kids were having a respite from paradise, tearing up the town with their awful young lives.

THE TURN OF THE YEAR

Pauline Holdstock

WINTER

At the far northern tip of the peninsula, where small farms ploughed right up to the hemlock woods, lived Hannah and her young son, Joseph.

INTERIOR HANNAH'S HOUSE FRONT ENTRANCE LATE DAY
HANNAH is dressing JOSEPH and herself for the cold, pulling on hat, boots etc. HANNAH concentrates on the clothes, trying not to look too much at the boy. Beside them, there is a suitcase on the floor round which a large Irish wolfhound worries excitedly. The sound of the dog's claws on the wooden floor is very distinct.

Hannah and her son were inseparable. He was all she had, she told herself fiercely and without sentiment. To her husband Ted, she put the matter more succinctly. "If you take him away, you'll kill me," were the words she chose to use.

But one day her husband did take the child away, albeit with the sanction of the courts, and on that day Hannah did, in a manner of speaking, cease to be.

EXTERIOR HANNAH'S DRIVE DUSK SLEETY RAIN
From behind the closed window of the car JOSEPH is calling repeatedly:
   —'Bye, Malachi! 'Bye, Malachi! 'Bye Malachi!
HANNAH, getting in, is muttering under her breath:
   —Damn dog!

It was the last day of the year when she gave up her son, handing him over in the airport lounge, the goods delivered, and she drove home in a falling rain, the sky streaming, her eyes streaming, the cars thinning, getting fewer and fewer the farther she drove until she was alone, heading out alone, for the north end of the peninsula.

At six o'clock, the time the plane was due to take off, she switched on the radio, as if, should there be a crash, the news of it would somehow be relayed instantly and she would hear of it. But the radio only crackled and fizzed like a damp firework.

"Damn," said Hannah. "Damn radio. Damn rain. Damn dog. Damn airport. Damn husband." And then, as an afterthought: "Ex-husband."

She drove on. The road ahead was as black as the sky but Hannah thought only of the boy, saw him in sunshine, saw him running, light as a bird, laughing. She did not usually pray but tonight she addressed the whole wet, night sky:

"Make him be safe. Make him be safe. Oh, God, if you're there, make him be safe."

INTERIOR HANNAH'S HOUSE EVENING
HANNAH is sitting with her feet drawn up on the edge of a chair, rocking. The dog, Malachi, lies with its chin pressed flat on the floor and watches her.

"Malachi!" Hannah made the dog jump with the sudden shrillness of her voice. "Malachi, I can't stand it! I'm going out — yes, O-U-T: walkies — and I'm going to be out there when that plane touches down two thousand miles away. I'm going to be *with* him."

EXTERIOR COUNTRY LANE NIGHT SLEETY RAIN
HANNAH is walking with the dog, reluctant now, at her heels. She is
striding out, unconscious of the cold rain or of the depth of darkness on
either side of the straggly hedgerows.

At exactly nine thirty-five she stopped. The sleet was no longer falling. The plane would have touched down.

Now.

Purposeful and calm, Hannah took a deep breath, turned round and started home. The rain had stopped; there was no sound but that of her own footsteps and the dog's. After the rustle of the sleet, the quiet of the December night was vast. It felt as if the sky had disappeared and the eye of God was watching from the emptiness beyond. It felt lonely beyond belief.

"Soon home, Malachi," said Hannah. But when she looked Malachi was not there. She whistled. There was no sound anywhere.

Cursing the dog under her breath, Hannah walked on. But there again was the sound of his paws on the gravel, as distinct as if he were by her side.

She stopped and whistled again, louder this time. The silence all around was so deep that she could, she thought, even hear his breathing. She walked on quickly, annoyed.

At the drive, she could still hear him, but the sound of his feet, his breathing, seemed to be growing more distant. The sounds were receding.

Hannah whistled now as loudly as she could. When she stopped, the only sound she heard, in all the world it seemed, was her own whistle echoing minutely inside her head.

INTERIOR HANNAH'S HOUSE KITCHEN MORNING
HANNAH is making breakfast. She is whistling softly, as if self-
consciously. When the toast is ready she sits down and breaks it into a
heap of tiny pieces.

It snowed in the night. When Hannah woke up, the walls and ceiling of her room were shining with reflected light. She stood at the window and looked out at the dazzling obliteration. There was nothing but mounding whiteness, blank, absolute.

Hannah went straight downstairs and opened the back door. The snow was unmarked by any tracks. Its light filled all the sky.

"No good whistling now, Malachi," she said softly, "is it?"

She had her breakfast of a mug of strong black coffee and took the toast out to the birds.

The rest of the day cannot be said to have passed as days do pass; it existed in a state of suspension, embalmed in snow.

To Hannah this seemed wholly appropriate, especially with Malachi gone. He'd taken himself off before like this. After some bitch in heat, she told herself. She did not like to think of him crunching rabbits and squirrels under the pine trees. She spent her time chopping wood and listening to mournful arias on the stereo. There was still no radio. When toward evening the loneliness of the previous night edged back and Hannah tried to call an old friend, she found the line was out of order and she was glad. "Good," she said and she stacked the stove full of wood and went to bed.

The dog did not return and Hannah began to feel uneasy in her isolation. With the snow already melted by a warm Pacific wind, the remains lying in patches under the hedges like shadows on a negative, Hannah drove up to the general store by the highway, watching out for Malachi on the way. The store was closed. That it should close for a few days after the New Year did not surprise Hannah. She still, nevertheless, needed milk.

"To the farm, James. To the farm." She turned abruptly to the empty seat beside her. "Not much of a wag, are you, James?" she said.

EXTERIOR A NEIGHBOUR'S FARM DAY
*Lights are on in the farmhouse. There is a truck in the driveway;
HANNAH's car is parked by the truck. HANNAH is at the house. She
knocks on a window and calls:*
— Anybody home? Marg? Time to get up. Good party?
There is no answer and HANNAH walks over towards the barn.

It was disconcerting to find no animals. Hannah decided that
the Bryces were away, their animals boarded at a friend's farm
perhaps. It did not seem a very satisfactory explanation but it
might — or it might not — account for the lights' being left on in
a house that was all locked up. Hannah assumed it *was* all locked
up. She was reluctant to try the door. It would not help, after all.

She got back in the car and began to reverse down the long
drive.

"All right, James. We are not amused. A farm, James. Take
me to a farm. One with geese and ducks ... quack ... and a fat
pig ... oink, oink ... and above all ... a great ... big ... mother of
a cow so I can put some ... *milk* in my coffee!"

And while she was at it, she thought, she could use the phone.
She would call the police and see if any strays had been run over,
picked up, sighted.

But the next farm was as quiet as the first. There were lights
here too, a porch light and one at a side door. Hannah thought
she heard the rusty squawk of a chicken but it was only a branch
creaking as the wind squeezed it against the roof of a shed.

There were no animals; this time Hannah did not need to go
and look.

Instead, she drove straight home and once inside the house
went to the phone. It was still out of order. She could not stop the
dial tone, no matter which numbers she tried to call.

"Who needs people?" she said and put the phone down
shakily.

The next day Hannah made a list:
> 1. Find someone
> 2. Find Malachi
> 3. Find a phone
> 4. Find some milk

Pausing for a moment she wrote carefully:
> 5. I think you can cope, don't you?
> 6. Yes

She spent the rest of the morning visiting her neighbours, systematically. By lunch time she gave up.

Sitting in her kitchen again, warming her hands on a mug of black coffee and staring at the list, she had an urge to change number six from "yes" to "no". Instead, she forced herself to be rational. It was a local evacuation. She told herself it had to be.

In the afternoon she drove out further, listening to the crackle of the radio, watching for cars that were not stationary, not empty. She found a service station, it too with its lights on, and filled her car with gas. There was no one to pay. She thought of leaving twenty dollars on the cash desk but she changed her mind and drove on. Once she thought she saw a bird fly up from beside the road, but it was only a dark scrap of paper, blown by the wind.

Again she returned home early in the precipitate dark, and this time she locked all the doors and double-checked them.

EXTERIOR CORNER STORE WINTER MORNING
The end of a two-by-four smashes through the glass, setting the alarm ringing. HANNAH knocks out the rest of the glass to reach inside for the lock.

"And two litres of milk please. Cream? Why not?" Hannah had almost filled her box from the store's fridge. "I do think it adds a little oomph to a dreary can of peaches, don't you? I knew you'd agree. Eggs, thank you. Cheese, thank you. Thank you very much."

She pushed the full box along the floor, singing:
    "Thank you very much for the food we're eating.
    Thank you very much,
    Thank you very, very, very, much."
At the door she lifted the box to carry it over the broken glass and out to the car.

EXTERIOR CORNER STORE BRIGHT WINTER SUN
The trunk is already full with three boxes of canned and dry goods.
HANNAH drives home without closing the trunk. The alarm in the
store is still ringing.

SUMMER

EXTERIOR HANNAH'S GARDEN SUMMER DAY
HANNAH is seated at a table out-of-doors. She is dressed as for a
summer luncheon. There are flowers on the table, and wine. Music is
coming from the open windows of the house. HANNAH, very animated,
is talking as she eats.

"Oh, it was dreadful, just *dreadful*. I couldn't believe it. Oh, yes. I drove all round the island. All round. Not a soul. Not ... a ... soul." She poured more wine. "You've no idea. Well, one just goes to pieces, absolutely to pieces. More salmon? Yes it is nice, isn't it? I was quite lucky to get hold of it."

She picked up the can of salmon and scraped the last flakes onto her plate. "What was I saying? Oh, yes. Well to begin with I just lay around in bed. You know how it is. I lived like a slut, really. Let everything go. Almost everything."

FLASHBACK TO:
INTERIOR HANNAH'S KITCHEN WINTER MORNING
HANNAH extremely dishevelled in housecoat. Boxes, cartons of food all over the floor, dishes in the sink. Books, papers, dirty cups on every available surface. HANNAH removes a plate of food from a small oasis of order on the table. She scrapes it into a full garbage bag and puts a fresh plate in its place. She does the same with a mug of milk, tips it away, replaces it. She repeats the procedure with the dog's food. Finally she slips her bare feet into boots and goes out to the garden with some bread. A midden of crusts has formed under the feeder.

"One thing, though," she leaned forward intently. "Do you know I never let go of the time. Not once. Oh, yes, incredibly difficult. Well it's like being in solitary, tremendously difficult to keep track. But do you know what I did?"

She leaned further forward, secretive now and drunk. "I wrote his name — no, not Ted's — Joseph's. I wrote his name every day. Once every day. On the wall.' Her gestures were grand. "When I came to my senses I had seventy-nine 'Joseph's' to clean off. Can you imagine? In lipstick."

She took another drink of wine and looked up suddenly, in surprise, "Now? Well I use a calendar now just like anyone else. Oh, I know," she said, opening another can. "It's amazing what you can do when you put your mind to it. But I'm lucky. I have electricity, you see, and my wood stove. And my music. Do you like this? Gluck's *Chaconne*. Nice isn't it? I treated myself. It is my birthday after all. I went into town — I don't often get there these days —"

FLASHBACK TO:
EXTERIOR TOWN SUMMER DAY
HANNAH'S car is in the middle of the deserted street, the door of the car open. There is glass on the sidewalk; alarms are ringing. HANNAH is beside the car. She is turning round and round, screaming at the blank windows of the buildings.

"— and I picked up a few records.

"And I've planted a kitchen garden. And did I tell you I'm teaching myself navigation? From the library of course. Well I just let myself in. What else could I do. I stamp them out at least. Don't always get them back on time, though. Never did. Yes, the garden's doing very well, very well indeed. I'll let you have some raspberries this year; they're just full of bloom. Well I know there are no bees," she poured the last of the wine, "but they'll find a way. We manage without them, after all ..."

INTERIOR BEDROOM NIGHT
HANNAH is undressed. She is standing in front of a long mirror, her palms, her breasts, her forehead pressed to the glass. Her eyes are closed.

WINTER

There had been times of course when Hannah had considered getting off the island. But during that first winter, when the seas were high, Hannah had been able to think of other, less uncomfortable ways to commit suicide, if it should come to that.

And the warmer calmer seas of summer had not made any difference; even when she had her boat equipped and ready to go Hannah's feet stayed firmly planted on the island. If she ever did get away she knew what she would find. Or, to be more accurate, not find. Clearly this was no bomb, nor evacuation, nor even epidemic.

Exactly what it was she was not sure. It had occurred to her that it was all her own doing, that she might indeed be in control. But still there was a small voice that came from a great distance and suggested that she might be in control, yes — for the time being — but she was nevertheless being watched, most closely.

Her rational mind told her bluntly that she was mad.

And yet she never gave in. It was not a question of courage; it was just that it would be like walking out of a movie — and Hannah always stayed until the end. How long it would take to reach the end of this one she did not know — but she was determined to see it through.

And so from day to day, through all the surprising spring, throughout the green and leafy summer and on into the bitter, barren autumn, Hannah had continued to survive. Sometimes she would drive back to the deserted town, setting alarms ringing as she took what she wanted from the stores, music mainly, choral works that she played at full volume, sending the choirs like angel voices over the empty fields.

Later in the year the feeling would come to her, more and more often, of a day charged with a sense of imminence; Hannah would get up and set her house in an expectant kind of order, clearing the debris of her living from the rooms, resurrecting old rituals and settings that would pronounce reality.

But these days at their close were as barren as the plants outside.

Then, as the days grew colder, Hannah spent her time collecting wood to fill the stove; and she would sit there beside it, every day the same, listening to it, feeling its warmth, waiting, remembering.

EXTERIOR AIRPORT WINTER DUSK
The only sound is the wind. HANNAH is beside her car, shivering. She is staring through the fence at the empty terminal, the great planes abandoned on the tarmac like bugs frozen in the icy wind.

In time came the day she waited for, the last of the year.

She got up early. When dawn came it was a thinning of the dark, no more, and the day was drab and chill. Hannah walked for a while but the silence was too large and she returned to the house to sit in front of the stove again and listen to its soft roar. She stared at the heavy sky and she waited.

At about four o'clock the sun found a breach in the cloud and leaked its pink all over the west. Hannah decided that waiting was not enough. She could not last another year, would not in fact live another day alone.

She put her head in her hands and closed her eyes. She had to make it work, would make it work. They were all there waiting in the falling dark, strangers, friends, lovers she had known, did not yet know, her son ...

She didn't know which to imagine first. She didn't know whether she should start with God. She didn't know if all she could imagine was herself imagining.

While her eyes were still closed, the first flakes of white drifted down on the dark.

Hannah started, so intently had she been listening for the sound of falling snow.

THE LAST FLIGHT
Michael Elcock

HE didn't really want to come all the way out to western Canada. He knew he was sick, that he didn't have very long. From time to time he was in pain, and he got tired easily.

I phoned him in England and said I'd be over on the mainland the day he arrived. Did he want me to wait a couple of hours and meet him at Vancouver International? *Oh yes, he said, surprised. I'd like that if it's not too much trouble.* He'd never have asked me to come over and meet him; never have compromised his independence.

What flight are you booked on to the island? I asked. *Oh, I haven't booked one yet. I never do. I always take the next one available, depending on how long it takes me to get through customs.* Would you like me to arrange one for you then? You can pay me back when you get here, I added, mindful of his independence. *Yes, he agreed. That would be the easiest way to do it.*

He'd worked for the airlines all his life; signed on as a kid before the war with Imperial Airways at Croydon Airport; gone to work in the big white Art Deco terminal as an office boy, watched the great Gothas and Hannibals drop out of the sky, drifting like clouds down onto the grass airfield. After flying with the RAF during the war he'd gone back to the airline, which was now called BOAC and he'd spent the rest of his working life overseas, running stations in places like Kaduna and Calcutta, Beirut, Caracas, Lisbon, Montego Bay, Delhi. Now as one of the senior retired ex-personnel he could have a first -class ticket anywhere he wanted to go. But he was always reluctant to ask for one, feeling somehow that it was taking advantage.

I hadn't really had any plans to go to the mainland at all and when the time came I called up the local airline. "It's one hundred eighty dollars," the clerk said.

"Each? I can almost fly to Europe for that."

"Sorry. If you'd booked twenty-one days in advance it would be cheaper."

"Thanks," I said, "I'll think of something else."

I phoned the harbour floatplane companies and the helijet. They weren't any better, or their schedules didn't fit with Dad's flight time. I called the charter companies at the airport. A fellow at one of them was keen.

"We'll take you over and back for three hundred and eighty," he said. "We can leave when you want and you'll have an hour on the ground at the other end without any extra charge. Not that we're too sticky about time," he added. "We can give you some leeway on that."

"That sounds as if it might work," I told him, doing the arithmetic in my head. One hundred and eighty dollars times two equals three hundred and sixty, and then the taxes and airport "improvement" fees. It would work out about the same.

"Of course, you can take some passengers along with you if you want," he added. "The airplane's got seven seats and the price is the same whether you use one of them or all seven." That clinched it.

"Okay, what do you need from me?"

"Credit card, that sort of thing." When it was all done he said,"Right, we'll see you at the old Air Force part of the airfield at five pm. If it's a fair evening it should be a nice flight."

It was a clear October night when we walked out to the airplane; cold and a sky bright with stars. The pilot introduced himself on the tarmac. His name was James. "The moon should be up soon," he said. "It's a full moon tonight." We climbed into a little twin-engined Piper Bonanza and arranged ourselves in the comfortable seats. The airplane had a roomy, wide cabin, sloping up towards the nose. James looked very young.

He turned in his seat and spoke to my daughter Xan. "Would you like to come up and sit in the co-pilot's seat?" She jumped up there in a second and quickly strapped herself in as if she'd done it a hundred times before. She was eleven. "Here, put these on," he said, handing her a set of earphones and a mike. "Press this button if you want to talk to me." He showed her. I could see her eyes widen. She knew her Grandad had been a pilot in the war and now she was going to feel what it was like.

We took off to the northeast over the town of Sidney, laid out in street-lit squares. The islands and the mainland rose up ghost-like in the windscreen as we climbed higher and soon mountains stretched from one horizon to the next, white with snow, glistening in the starlight like a frosted fence up and down the mainland coast.

We skirted Saltspring Island and then the moon poked out from the side of Mount Baker, enormous and rose-coloured and moving as we watched it. I held my breath. It climbed out of the mountain which stands head and shoulders above all the others on that stretch of coast and began to ascend into the night sky, changing gradually to the colour of oatmeal.

"It's a Bomber Moon," I whispered, more to myself than anyone else. "It knows Dad's coming."

The Gulf Islands slid past below us, laid out a lighter shade of dark on a black, gunmetal sea. Lights twinkled from houses, small villages. The pilot asked Xan if she wanted to fly the airplane and she did, and he gave her a twenty-minute lesson as we flew on over the islands and entered onto the long black stretch over the Georgia Strait. "Take it to the left," he told her and she banked twenty degrees and we slid off to the left. "Now straighten out," and she did that. "Back onto your heading now," he said, "we're flying a course of thirty-seven degrees. Watch your height, we don't want to climb over three thousand five hundred … " And so on and she loved it all, every minute of it.

"You mustn't shoot too much of a line about it at school tomorrow," I told her when we were driving over in the taxi to the main terminal at Vancouver International. "The other kids won't like you for it."

"You mean I can't tell anyone I was flying the plane?" she said.

"No, that's not what I mean. I just mean you mustn't overdo it."

Her Grandad came round the corner from customs with his case; looking older than when I'd seen him in the summer, looking frail. He saw me and smiled and came toward the gate. Em and Xan were standing further back at the place he'd have to pass when he came out into the public part of the terminal. I waved and moved to where they were. He almost dropped his bag when he saw them he was so pleased. *I'd never have recognised you, he said to Xan. You've grown so much since I saw you.*

At the other terminal, the little commercial one where the Piper Bonanza was waiting, we walked out on to the tarmac. *Where are you taking me? he asked. This is all a bit of a surprise.*

"Well, we thought we'd go back in this," I said as we walked up to the little airplane. "Do you want to sit up beside the skipper? He said it's all right with him if you want to." *I don't know if I should.* "It's all right," I said, knowing he was thinking about the rules in these matters.

I helped him up on to the wing and he climbed awkwardly into the co-pilot's seat. I watched the difficulty he was having and thought about the picture I have of him sitting high up in the pilot's seat of his bomber, young and bold and smiling; only a little bit more than a boy.

When we were in the air the pilot asked him if he wanted to take the controls, but Dad just smiled and said that was fine; he'd just watch if it was all right. I could see him sitting up there with the headphones on, checking over the dials, gazing out of the window from time to time at the dark islands, nodding his head and speaking as the pilot asked him questions.

We landed at Victoria International Airport thirty minutes later and there was a light in Dad's eye. He didn't say much about it, but he'd been alive again, up there in his element.

The pilot took me aside as we walked across the tarmac. "That was a real privilege," he said. "To fly with someone like that. Thank you. I mean it. Thanks."

Postscript:

My father stayed with us for two weeks and rested well. He had the best sleeps he'd had for months, he said. He woke up each night he said, and looked out of the window by his bed and saw Orion more clearly than he'd ever seen it before, even when he was flying. Then he went back to England and a little over a month later he died. Sometimes now I look up at Orion on winter nights and I imagine I can see the shadow of an old bomber passing across its face, and I think of him.

THE BENCH

Michael Cullen

YOU know how it is in the business. The Victoria Film Board gave Spielberg permission to do it in Victoria and threw in the perks: a floor of hotel suites at cost, help from the city to block off locations, provide escorts and security and, at the time, the promise of a dollar value at sixty percent of the American.

Though someone close to the source said that a documentary on benches was probably the single most important look at the formation of culture, Spielberg had to decline. Egoyan got second dibs, but after all the hoopla it was Stalarsky who got the nod and made the trip from LA with half the crew, two trucks with dashboards covered with significant pieces of paper — and no money.

"A story on benches must be done," Stalarsky announced. "It is where culture began; and where history followed. Bench it is!"

The big perk that Stalarsky didn't mention, of course, was the imminent death of Harold Pinston and how it fit into the picture.

Stalarsky might not have had all the awards, but he had his share of credits. Including the documentary *Dark and Stormy Night in*

Korea that some say was the real influence for *MASH*. And he chose Karen as the star. He promised she could sing. She practised the national anthem for days as the trucks drove along the highways.

Roman Kaplan handled the money and the business side for Stalarsky's production company. Kaplan was very smooth, had connections and managed to hire the expert on benches for a percentage of the profit. "I gave him a contract for two percent of the net," Kaplan said. "But I don't think he's in the business. 'Cause if he was, he'd know there's never any net." And that's how Charles Milken, the expert, came on the scene.

"Quiet, everybody. Quiet!"

"And … and … " Stalarsky waved his hand in the air like a conductor, pointed at the camera, then to Charles Milken, the expert, and dropped his hand.

Charles Milken began carefully, thoughtfully. "Culture, as we know, happened one day a long, long time ago at exactly three in the afternoon when someone somewhere felt secure enough, comfortable enough, strong enough, and full enough to sit down. Let's call him 'Ed.' Ed sat down. His tummy was full, his landscape was safe, his muscles were strong, his women and children taken care of. He sat. And do you know what he did? He looked around. For the first time ever, humankind went from action and reaction to contemplation. Ed sat on a *benc* — what we now call a bench. The horizon was there for him to contemplate. From a bench, culture was born."

The bench near the Empress Hotel, and beside the Tourist Information Bureau, had already been chosen by Karen — an obvious choice — but the guy with the puppets wouldn't let them film there in the early morning.

"It's where I live," he argued. "How'd you like someone filming your house at seven in the morning?"

"Fine," Stalarsky said, and turned to his small band of assistants who followed him everywhere. "Let's find another location."

"Karen won't like this," one assistant mumbled. "She'll bring out the stick. Trust me."

"She doesn't have a stick," another corrected. "She's not allowed."

"We don't have any money," the techie sound-man said. "The crew hasn't been paid, no one's been fed, and our cards are completely maxed."

"Fine," Stalarsky said. "Kaplan promised we would have the money. But, to start with, let's find somewhere cheap. There's always food and help somewhere cheap."

"Sooke's cheap," someone suggested.

An assistant shook his head. "It's where the end meets itself. And the last glance is the same as the first."

The managers of the three big hotels along the inner harbour phoned the mayor, the Royal Canadian Mounted, the Chamber of Commerce and the Victoria Film Board, but by the time they got the puppet man removed, Stalarsky had packed the trucks and was gone. By now, Karen had been told that the location was being moved. She said she was glad, because the Sooke area "is a place with wind where people do not understand the purpose of language. And I do not want to sing there."

"Just give me a name with a location," Stalarsky said angrily.

"Sidney's cheap," an assistant said. "They have over thirty benches. And five of them have statues attached. But most important, Harold Pinston is there. He'll give us the money if we use his memorial bench. That's who the bagman is getting the money from."

"Fine," Stalarsky said and jumped into the front of the sound truck. "I want Harold Pinston's bench in every frame. Where's Sidney?"

A group from the sewing and weavers' club sat in a semi-circle under an apple tree down and to the left of the bench.

"Start filming immediately, and don't stop. That way, we might finish the documentary before we realize we don't have any money to do it. What are they doing?" Stalarsky asked and pointed.

"They're knitting," an assistant replied. "Apparently they come out to all the cultural events in the community. National Geographic calls them one of the significant archetypal moments in the creation of culture. They're very quiet."

"Fine," said Stalarsky. "Is there any way we could charge them money?"

Harold Pinston was the money. Harold's lawyer had his hand on the zipper. Kaplan put the whole thing together. It was called "working capital". Here was the deal. Harold Pinston was ninety-three years old and dead, or almost dead. He was so dead, his doctor sent him home from the hospital. And Pinston had been making unsolicited advances, most particularly to the night shifters. "Send him home to Resthaven," the doctor had said, "and he can do whatever he wishes to his furniture, himself, the wildlife in the area and his neighbours."

"Who wouldn't want to die on a street with a name like Resthaven?" Harold's lawyer said. "I hope he feels that sentiment and is able to embrace it quickly."

Harold had a bundle of money: he wanted a bench as a memorial. The bench was already located at the spot where he had his morning coffee — down at a small park near the new wharf. Provided his bench was actually the focus of the documentary, Harold wanted his estate to bankroll the film. The catch was that the money from his estate wouldn't be released until he died. It was Harold's final dream. A bench, *the* bench, the spot of contemplation for humankind, the bench that would indeed be the benchmark from which all other benches on earth would be measured. His bench. Harold's bench. Harold reckoned his memorial would live forever.

Charles Milken, the expert: "The word bench comes, of

course, from the old English *benc*, a bank — a mound-like formation or a raised portion of a river, lake or ocean. The seat of a bench is traditionally made from wood. The top of the seat is raised from sixteen to eighteen inches; the most comfortable height, on average, seems to be about sixteen and a half inches. When you sit on a bench, you will notice that the most comfortable leg position happens when the bottom of your knee — which is bent — is slightly above the top of the bench seat."

Roman Kaplan was actually a cousin of Stalarsky's. Kaplan had been the bagman for a number of important documentaries including *In Search of Tse-Tses*, a mega-project that attempted to discover the migratory patterns of the famous tse-tse fly. As mentioned, he connected with Harold Pinston and Pinston's lawyer and struck the deal.

"We have the money as soon as Pinston dies," Kaplan assured. "It's in the bag."

"Is he dead?" the sound techie asked.

"He's not actually dead, yet," Kaplan said. "But he's so close, doornail close, that we can start shooting anytime."

"Is he dead?" Stalarsky asked.

"Well, actually, he's not quite dead."

"Karen won't like this," an assistant mumbled. "If she starts to sing with the stick, there will be trouble."

"Can we take the chance that he will die very soon?"

"Definitely," Kaplan said. "We're already shooting. I've got a line of credit at the hotel near the wharf, at the food store across the street, at the cold beer outlet somewhere down the road, and the mayor would like to have a brief news conference with a small photo shoot for the local paper. And three real estate agents have a garden tour slated for us next Wednesday evening, time permitting of course."

"How dead is he?"

"He's promised me personally that he will be dead within three days. And so did his lawyer."

"Fine," said Stalarsky. "How much will the bank advance us until Pinston dies?"

"Unfortunately, zilch. They pretended they didn't know who you are."

"Credit union," an assistant said. "If there's a donut shop, there's a credit union."

"Hit the credit union, then — for an advance," Stalarsky directed Kaplan. "And I want it by four o'clock."

"The good news is that they're usually open until six," the assistant added and smiled and nodded twice.

"And Harold Pinston is pretty much dead, right?" Stalarsky asked.

"Bank on it," Kaplan nodded.

Nobody noticed the girl, who had walked up the slight incline from the water. The tide was in: the rocks around the bottom were slippery and covered with barnacles. It was difficult to see how she got there in the first place unless she came by small boat. She had seaweed stuck to her legs. She stood at a distance, like a watery statue, and looked about.

Milken, the expert: "A standard bench, perhaps with a bit of a contoured roll, has a seat height of sixteen to eighteen inches, an overall height of forty inches and an overall depth of twenty-six inches. Over time and worldwide, the standard two-by-four has also become the standard wood. The 'two' comes from a normal thumb length. The 'four' comes from a middle finger length from the centre of the knuckle to the end of the finger where the nail stops." Milken placed his closed fist with his middle finger raised toward the camera.

"Cut!" cried Stalarsky.

He walked forward. "We're trying to sell this to the National Film Board, not Mr Fix-It." He stared at Milken. "And what's with this?" Stalarsky raised his middle finger at Milken.

Karen arrived. "I've just been with my diaphragm therapist, and she insists that I sing at least once during the documentary. Or twice. She said twice."

"Did you hurt yourself?," Stalarsky asked. He pointed to the walking stick she had.

Karen looked at the stick. "Oh this? No. I bought it from a town crier. Nice, isn't it." She rubbed the knob on the top.

"You know you're not allowed to carry sticks on the set. It's been in the contract since that incident in Maui."

"It's not a stick, it's a walking stick. Anyway, I have faced my old demons and have completely individuated."

"I was at the meeting when you agreed to not carry any more sticks," Kaplan said.

"Well, I couldn't resist this one. This morning, I ran into a town crier, and it was outside the fish restaurant and he was dressed like a pirate and I said I simply had to have his walking stick. He said he simply couldn't part with it, so I offered him fifty American."

"And that was it?"

"Well, actually, I offered him fifty American and a part."

"A what?" Stalarsky yelled.

"A very small speaking part."

"No."

"He just walks on, says 'Hear ye!' and then he walks off. That's it. Please?"

"No."

"Look!" Karen said tightly, suddenly. She lifted the stick and jabbed it at Kaplan. "I could swing this thing."

"Not again." Kaplan moved back a few steps.

"No," said Stalarsky.

"No means no Karen either. And if I'm not the star, there is no star."

Stalarsky shook his head. He bit nervously on a piece of skin from his thumb. "Fine," he said. "Fine."

At that moment, the ballerina in the ivory-white tutu and white pointed shoes glided across the grass in front of the bench and performed three jetés forward, then pirouetted and returned with three more jetés.

The accountant was provided to the production company gratis as a goodwill gesture by the local whale museum.

"You're still all right below the line," the accountant said. "That's because you don't have anything below the line. Above the line, though, there's nothing but red lights. You still haven't paid back the money you borrowed from the kids on the street corner playing their violins."

"Anything else?" Stalarsky asked, and chewed from a piece of bakery multi-bagel.

"You might think about terminating the star."

"Karen?"

"She's too expensive. She's too demanding. She just ordered a portapotty for the set and has demanded a Broadway chorus for the bandstand. She said the acoustics couldn't be ignored."

Stalarsky nodded. "Fine," he said. "I'll have my people talk to her people."

"Okay, let's shoot the expert," Stalarsky said. He raised his hand, then dropped it slowly. "And ... !"

"Many benches are part of a 'recycling loop' which, in a way, takes urban trees called 'rediscovered wood products' and makes benches from them. As you look at the bench on which I sit —"

"Cut!" Stalarsky called. "All this is fine, but this bench is made of concrete."

"I'm leading to the point where it doesn't matter, the composition of the bench. The bench becomes form that is eternal. The bench is floating furniture. What it is made from is mortal, mutable. Its space, though, is eternal. Its composition is incidental. Think sand," Charles Milken said. "It's sand reinventing itself. See the world in a grain of sand."

"I don't care," Stalarsky says. "This isn't about how to use floating cement and then ignoring what you've made from it, is it?"

Milken smiled. "I think you're beginning to understand …
It's a significant documentary about a bench. It is not a significant
documentary that uses the bench as an object of the 'whoosh'."

"Let me glance at the script," Pinston's lawyer said.

"There is no script," an assistant with small, round glasses
explained. "Stalarsky works from the posture of natural
improvisational. His documentaries are ideologically brilliant
because they are directed by themselves, by their own need to
'be', by the abundant world which comes from them, and by
Stalarsky's own genius ability to edit and add sound. He has the
artist's touch. And that touch of intertextuality knows when to
stop, to leave alone, and not to touch. The touch, itself, is a touch-
not."

"I wonder if Pinston knows what he's gotten into," Pinston's
lawyer said.

The sound techie approached Stalarsky. "The Victoria
Independent Film and Video Festival wonders if they can premier
the documentary at the local cinema here."

Stalarsky looked thoughtfully at the piebald sky, then at the
ocean, then the bench. "No," he mumbled. "No."

"The bench. Harold Pinston's bench is a simple, clean, classic
example. Usually the length of a human body, the height equal
to the length from the knee to the ankle on an average adult living
at a particular time in history, the width from the bottom of the
back and along the hamstring to five centimeters or two inches
back from the back of the knee."

"Cut! What's that?" Stalarsky pointed. A row of small tents
had been pitched overnight.

"Oh, that's the Sidney Rotary," an assistant explained.

"If they arrive on their scooters, we cut," Stalarsky ordered.
"And I don't want them to do any figure eights."

"They don't have scooters. They use tents to make money for

charity," Karen interrupted. "Each tent has a simple game of skill that fills the coffers with coin."

"We're not the circus!" Stalarsky said.

"Don't yell at me."

"I didn't."

"Don't."

"I didn't." Stalarksy turned to an assistant. "See if we can borrow some money from the roulette wheel. The credit union stiffed us."

"And … and … " Stalarsky called, raised his hand toward the bench, then to the camera, then slowly lowered his hand.

"This is a good bench," Milken the expert said. He pointed at it. Then at the inscription. "A good bench in the right place gets outside itself. A good bench disappears. It's different from other furniture. When you connect with it physically, it ceases to exist. The only thing we put on it is our consciousness. Our transcendent self. Whoosh. Whoosh. There is no weight. There is only nothing and everything.

"When you look out from a bench, the vista transports you. It becomes reflexive. It returns to you as part of you. The bench then is gone. Your moment is the place; the place floats away with your eyes and returns to your eyes. And something happens. You stop time. You stop the whirlygig. You literally get off the bus. And everything that is and everything that was suddenly melts into your being. The words on the inscription and what they lead to are as alive as what the body on the bench stretches out to. Whoosh. "

"And, the most important bench," Stalarsky called, then turned to his first camera. "Keep rolling. Keep rolling. Don't cut."

"The most important bench in the world? It's the bench which faces midway between east and west and north and south in a perfect ratio, and in a perfect astrological location between the binaries of Apollo and Diana." Milken rubbed his hand along the bench, then looked at the bench and smiled. "This is it. This, like ten million other benches everywhere, is the only one."

The skateboarder slipped toward the bench, ollied over it, onto it, grinded the rail, jumped. It sounded like a small train. Two butts, both rollies wedged loose. Landed perfectly.

"I want the basic component of life on the bench," Stalarsky said. "A single cell that has come from the salt water to land. Let's start there. And then I want to build until all the parts of humankind are represented."

The seagull moved off, toward the water.

"Somebody clean that," Karen directed. "And get that splotch over the back ... ya, there."

Nobody noticed the girl, who had walked up the slight incline from the water. She moved past the small tents, past the knitters, past the light stands, the mike boom, the techies and the sound crew toward the bench. She had seaweed stuck to her legs. She seemed to be smiling.

Meanwhile, his worship, the mayor:

"Hi," he says. "On behalf of the citizens and councillors, it is my pleasure to welcome you to Sidney by the Sea."

"Cut!" Stalarsky yelled. The entire set froze. "Who the hell is this?"

"Mayor. I'm the mayor." The mayor stepped forward and pressed his hand toward Stalarsky. "I'm the bearer of a great gift ... the keys to the town."

"Who are they?" Stalarsky called and pointed to a group of people watching the filming.

"They are onlookers. Potential extras looking for a break into the film business."

"How come they look oldish?"

"The acting classes from the local schools will be bused in tomorrow."

"Where's Kaplan?" Stalarsky called.

"He's gone to the hotel, the one on the water," Karen apologized. "Apparently they bulldozed his room this morning. He's in great distress."

"Give them some free tickets to *The Young and the Restless*," Stalarsky said. "Then maybe they will go away."

"Most of them are employees of the bookstore," Karen said.

"It's the largest employer in the area after some places that make iron products," said the mayor.

"And people who make acid," muttered an assistant.

"So?"

"We don't have any tickets," Karen said .

"Fine. *The Price is Right* then. *The Price is Right*."

"We don't have them either."

"Okay. Are there any Canadian shows they want to see?"

"Maybe *The Musical Ride* ..."

"And, as the mayor of this wonderful community, I welcome you. We are indeed a town that has many benches. 'Sit and rest awhile,' one of them says. And we appreciate the bounty our local businesses reap whenever a major film company uses our panoramic vistas and town sites as part of their production. Vive le bench!"

"Ask the Royal Mounted if we can get a colour guard," an assistant suggested. "Then hit them for some freebees."

"And now, if I may, I am pleased to give these keys to you that unlock Beacon Avenue, both directions one way, including the fish market and the frames on the sides of the building with or without pictures."

Stalarsky cued. Charles Milken continued. "You have heard people say 'that's my bench'. Actually, that's not really a territorial imperative. It's a note, a post-it to the universe that what they have seen, felt and interiorized on that bench is theirs. It's very individual: it's something that involves everything and yet is not shared. It is beyond words: no dialogue can explain it. So, when someone low on the food chain marks up a bench, uproots a bench, hurts or violates a bench, they violate the eternal universal. The bench is almost incidental to the anger and the wrath that results from graffiti."

"Cut!" Stalarsky called. "That comment about 'low on the food chain' could insult quite a few." He turned to his techies. "Don't send the press book or the trailer anywhere north of here."

"I went around town and collected empties like you asked," the techie told Stalarsky. "I got fourteen dollars and twenty-five cents at the bottle depot."

"Fine," said Stalarsky.

"Do you want me to buy food ... or beer."

"It's the Sidney branch of the Film Commission phoning from the BC Film Commission office," Kaplan yelled. "They phoned to see if we're the ones doing the docu-drama on Prince Charles."

"Tell them to bugger off," called Stalarsky. "Our theme is benches. Benches in Sidney."

"We, ah, perhaps we shouldn't be too hasty here," Kaplan suggested slowly. "They might have a budget."

"Fine," Stalarsky said. "Tell them we're the ones. Tell them we ... are ... the ones."

"I'm ahead of this," Kaplan said. "I took the initiative and employed the guy who built the cultural center to persuade the Prince to visit. All we need is some help, a stipend, a grant, some money, somebody local that looks like the Prince and the deal's done. At worst, we can get the Scouts to walk past and maybe show how to tie some knots. I also told them that this was the bench the Prince sat on."

Meanwhile, the girl wrapped in seaweed and barnacles wandered quietly around the periphery.

The camera embraced the wrinkled, thoughtful face of Charles Milken. He continued: "A chair has a beauty to it, an aesthetic. It allows you to sit and do something. A bench, though, allows you to sit and do nothing. The magic of doing nothing. Doing nothing, of course, is considerably different than doing dick."

"Cut," yelled Stalarsky. "No 'dick', if you don't mind. We're trying to pitch this to Hollywood and the Sundance Film Festival."

"They use dick all the time," Milken the expert argued.

"They don't use it the way you do," Stalarsky said.

"But I use it in the best possible way."

Milken scratched beside his left ear where a small mark from his glasses had begun to tan up.

"Exactly," Stalarsky said. "The larger world doesn't understand dick the way you understand dick. Understand?

"And ... and ... " Stalarsky's hand dropped like a slow, silk scarf.

"Again, then ... A bench allows you to sit and do nothing. The aesthetic is self-reflexive. When you look out, you end up looking in. It is the only furniture that allows for this. All other pieces of furniture have a purpose —a utility — that ultimately defines them.

"When I sit on this bench, I stare out across the water to the islands, to their green horizons and undefined silhouettes. I look as far as I can. And the entire panorama turns and returns and interrupts. The components are the bench. And the things on the bench all mesh and become a part of what has returned and what has left and what ever was and what ever will be. And time suddenly stops. Completely. Whoosh."

"Don't say whoosh!" Stalarsky said. "Cut! You said it earlier, too. Don't say whoosh!"

"Hear ye! Hear ye!"

"What?"

"Karen! Where's Karen?"

"Karen's right here, waiting to sing the national anthem," Karen said.

"Who is he?" Stalarsky yelled and pointed at the person dinging the bell in front of the bench. "He looks like Bluebeard or Pegleg or something."

"He's the town crier I bought the stick from," said Karen. "I promised him a couple of words."

"And ... ?"

"And he's done," Karen nodded, then waved to the crier.

"Tell him to stop ringing that bell," the sound techie called.

"Animator," Stalarsky announced. "We need an animator."

"Acrylic or pastels?" the volunteer from the local arts council asked. "We also have them in weaving. But nobody of significance does glass."

Stalarsky had seen a picture dangling near the self-help cream dispenser in a coffee shop. The one where everyone has very helpful teeth. "Get her," he said. "That artist. The one with the yellow birds and golden pears. If she can draw things that suspend, she can draw fluffy ducks that land on grass and eat bugs. Am I yes? Yes?"

The mayor and council of Sooke heard of the decision not to shoot in their area and sent a nasty letter to the production company. They demanded an apology they could run in the local paper.

"Fine," Stalarsky said. "Send a letter. Tell them we're doing a documentary on the Prince and Sooke didn't have adequate banquet facilities."

"And I'll send a letter to the National Film Board at the same time," the assistant said. "I'll see if they're interested in versioning the documentary into French."

"Do we want dubbing, voice-over or subtitles?" Stalarsky asked. "We could sell versioning rights to the Japanese and Germans, too."

"The printed word is so different from the spoken word," Milken the expert interrupted. "This might be the moment of crossover in a culture that has established its basic rituals and icons. And that means everything that comes from the bench, our bench, the first bench —"

"Just focus on this bench. We don't have enough money to do a cultural history of the world. Has anyone heard any sad news from Harold Pinston yet?"

"We were almost out of film," Kaplan said. He was out of breath. "But I managed to borrow some brand new reels from the organizers of the weekly dog show at the cultural center."

"Put them in the truck," Stalarsky pointed. "They are like gold to my eyes."

"We have enough to finish," Kaplan smiled. "We're in business at the bench."

"I need a tug. I want to have a small house on a barge that floats easily and softly across the water and, from a distance, becomes a red roof, yellow sides, purple haze pulled gently forever, a rose upon the water that blends as it moves the life within, the life around, the life above and the life below."

"There's a sailpast in December that would work," an assistant said.

"We don't have until December. We're out of here in a week."

"We could use the guy from the water taxi," another assistant said. "He's got a boat and sells jumbo smokies on the wharf. We could get him to put a large cardboard box on his boat and float slowly past. And we could use the smokies to go with the beer."

"Fine. Let's improvise. Let us think of the bench as that small house on a barge that is floating. Okay? Film the bench a little longer than ten frames," Stalarsky said. "I want the bench to linger as we float into the next sequence. Into every sequence. I want the bench to live in the mouths and words and actions of everything that happens." He turned to the techies. "It's called persistence of motion. You see an object for a split second longer than it is in front you. This way, we are being true to life as we linger in the minds of those who watch and feel and sit and as we discover the essence of culture."

At that moment, the ballerina in the ivory-white tutu and white pointed shoes glided across the grass in front of the bench and performed three jetés forward, then pirouetted and returned with three more jetés.

Harold Pinston arrives.

"You will notice that the crosspiece of wood was, at one time, hit by a bolt of lightning. If we could get a close-up of the spot, you will notice that the dark bruise emanates from a vortex." Milken pointed with his second finger. "That is the spot."

The still of the vortex coincided with the arrival of Harold Pinston.

Pinston, clearly, was not dead. Not even close. He moved slowly, though, uncertainly, but with a bit of confidence. His eyes seemed younger. He was propped by his lawyer.

"It's his last earthly wish," Pinston's lawyer explained.

Pinston was helped through the lines, past the Rotary game tents, through the knitters, past the sound and tech trailers, past the camera, toward the bench where Charles Milken stood.

"Has it got a plaque with my name on it?" Harold Pinston managed.

Someone tapped him to be quiet.

Karen seized the moment to step forward for a special "silent mood of time" on the bench, where she demanded a close-up and used her visage to suggest how immensely inspired she was, then jumped up quite suddenly and kicked her legs, a dance intro to a Celtic lilt. "You can almost hear bagpipes," a techie whispered, as if in prayer. Suddenly, she burst into a huge high note, like a Viking horn calling to the deserted sandbar that stretched like a pointing finger from the spit on Sidney Island.

The girl with the seaweed and barnacles on her legs sparked to life. She marched toward the bench, then, without permission, sidestepped around the dancing Karen, just behind Charles Milken, and sat.

"It hasn't hurt the strength of the structure, but rather … " Milken continued, slipping in front of Karen's swaying arms. He stopped, switched his eyes from the camera, and glared back at Karen. "You are assaulting the thoughts from my bench."

"Cut!" yelled Stalarsky.

Charles Milken, the expert, looked around the set, then at

Stalarsky, then to the bench. His eyes lit on the girl with seaweed and barnacles on her legs. "I'm in the middle of my close and distant thoughts," he announced. "I am the one that is within and without the bench. *I'm* the one on camera!"

"I will take a moment," Karen said quietly, tightly. "I am the star."

The girl with the seaweed rolled, seemed to smile, then stretched on the bench.

And Harold Pinston saw the girl with the seaweed slowly recline on his bench. He noticed her damp hair, and long, thin legs.

"It's his last wish," the lawyer said.

"Did you tell her she could say a few words too?" Stalarsky called out to Karen.

Karen's face slowly shaded. Her eyes tensed. Her lips pursed, then rose at the corners. She swallowed slightly. She tightened her hand around the walking stick.

"Did you say something nasty?" she whispered.

Harold Pinston shuffled towards the bench. He nodded, perhaps to the air, perhaps to the ocean, perhaps to the bench, then leaned on it. "My bench," he mumbled. "Mine." He looked down at the girl. "Mine."

"I said nothing," said Stalarsky.

Karen shook her head. "You yelled."

"I'll yell now! I'm Stalarsky!! Director of *Dark and Stormy Night in Korea*!! And I'll yell if I want to yell!"

Harold Pinston, meanwhile, had leaned over the back of the bench, lost his balance and fell over, onto the girl with the seaweed legs.

"Nobody yells at Karen," said Karen.

Somehow, Pinston managed to get his shirt off. He threw it, and it landed beside Stalarsky's foot. "Oh yes," Pinston mumbled through droopy, purple lips. "Ooooh yes."

"I think I should point out that my client is ninety-three years old and likewise is on top of a woman on the bench," Pinston's lawyer said. "And he seems to have taken off most of his clothing."

"Roll!" Stalarsky cried. "On the bench. Focus on the bench."

"We've been rolling since forever," an assistant called. "Since we got here."

"You told me I couldn't sing the national anthem," Karen said. She started swinging the stick.

"I didn't yell."

"Karen heard Stalarsky yell at Karen," she said.

Stalarsky took a step back, then two, then more, until he was trapped behind the bench. Karen loomed: "You said it would interrupt the flow."

Stalarsky swallowed. "Fine! You already sang. Sing again! Sing!"

"You yelled again!" Karen took a large stride, pulled the stick back, then swung it mightily through the air. Stalarsky ducked, at the very same moment that Harold Pinston seemed to look up, or glance up, or bob up.

Most thought that the stick hit Pinston on the side of his skull. The smack, though, seemed muted, as if it somehow missed and hit the concrete back of the bench instead. Nobody could say for certain. Nevertheless, Pinston dropped completely on top of the lady with the seaweed. Stalarsky stood, then turned. Pinston's lawyer ran forward. Karen dropped the stick. Roman Kaplan ran past her, just behind Pinston's lawyer, to the bench. Charles Milken, the expert, turned back to the bench to help.

Pinston's lawyer was the first to actually touch Pinston.

"He's … he's limp!" Pinston's lawyer exclaimed, and pulled his client from the bench so the lady with the seaweed could get up. "And the lady beneath seems to have lost some of her clothing!"

"He's smiling!" yelled Stalarsky.

Roman Kaplan was still smarting over his hotel room being bulldozed. ("And I hid two bottles of Saturna Island cabernet under my pillow.") Yet he managed to grab Pinston's wrist, to feel for a pulse.

"He's ... he's dead!" Pinston's lawyer said.

"Oh, oh no," Karen said quietly. She looked up at Pinston's lawyer. "Will the insurance cover both of them?"

The girl with the seaweed got up slowly. She looked about, smiled, bent slightly and rubbed Pinston's face with her left hand. Then she recovered her clothing and walked away, past the cameras and the gophers and the techies and the sound crew, over the thick black wires for the lights and the sound, past the boom of lights that looked like stars touching the long, flowing sun and the knitters and the tents of games, back down the incline toward the ocean.

"He's smiling." Pinston's lawyer frowned. "I don't think we can release the money. I can't tell if he's dead."

"Did I kill ... Is he dead?" asked Karen.

"I would need a medical certificate."

"We have one with the papers on the dash of the truck," an assistant said.

Roman Kaplan jumped in. "I will phone the bank and tell them Pinston is dead," he said. "He simply has to be. This is just tremendous news. We owe the food store and the cold beer outlet far more than I thought."

"Is he dead?" Stalarsky asked.

"I ... I think so." Pinston's lawyer bent low over Pinston's mouth, trying to hear a breath. "He keeps smiling."

"Fine. The bench must prevail. Declare him dead, whether he's dead or not. We'll have a memorial here at the bench. I will film the stripping of his plaque. And we can just take him with us when we leave."

The assistant handed Pinston's lawyer the certificate.

"In that case, I declare him dead."

The mayor stepped forward. "The benches cushion the sound from the planes that arrive and depart overhead. They allow us to hear the sounds from the shells and the sea and the shrimp and the crab and the orca and the greys. They call to us from the fog and from the horizon."

"Those are *my* lines," Charles Milken said.

"And this is the bench that eliminates all doubt and fills the heart with love. All the time that was, and all the time that is, has stopped. It is forever. Touch eternity. Sit on this bench. Become without. Float with me."

"So he's not dead?," Stalarsky asked.

Pinston's lawyer looked up. "He's either not dead … or he's dead," he said. "Either way, as his lawyer, I have seen the medical certificate and I release the money."

"Keep filming," Stalarsky called and waved his hand.

"I'm so relieved that he's dead," Karen sighed. "I thought I might have killed him. I am so glad I didn't but that he might be."

"Fine. Put him in the trailer with the cot where we keep the lights. Give him water and food if he needs them. And keep filming."

You know how it is in the business. The bagman Roman Kaplan went around with cheques and paid almost everybody the company owed. The mayor wanted another opportunity. The money was so in place that Stalarsky decided to stay for a few more days. He called the crew and actors.

"This is real-time documentary filming. We are doing a documentary about a bench in Sidney, the first sign of cultural significance in the history of humankind." He paused, then nodded knowingly at them. "There's no script. You are professionals. Karen is the star. I am the guide. I have the money. Now, let's do it. Let's sit, for a moment, or maybe two. And we'll start from scratch. But first, on the bench, let's sit."

MARGUERITE
Kathy Page

MARGUERITE, in daisy flip-flops, turquoise swimsuit and zebra-print kimono, stands at her new neighbour's front door. Her back is stiffly straight; her skin, intricately folded from top to toe, but for the burnished upper slope of her chest, is burned deep brown, mottled here and there with freckles and moles; even her scalp, visible beneath thinning, stiffly permed silver hair, shows her tan. As the door opens, she holds out her bunch of garden flowers — dahlias, small, dark-hearted sunflowers, some fern, their stems wrapped in foil.

"I am your neighbour Marguerite," she announces. "Welcome. I have come to visit you."

"Thank you," the new woman says, introducing herself as Jo. She apologizes for the smell of paint. She has no furniture, or rather, she explains, it is stuck in a warehouse in Vancouver. Her husband, Mark, is still in London, finishing his old job. Right now, the two children are at day camp ... She waves distractedly at the bare, newly-painted surfaces, takes the flowers, serves grape juice in picnic glasses. They sit in the main room, on garden chairs, the flowers, in a washed-out milk carton, displayed on the white plastic table between them.

Marguerite reaches across the table and grasps the younger woman's hand. She seems rather shy and she looks washed out,

Marguerite thinks. Too thin. No makeup, no tan, highlights growing out.

"I remember what it is like to arrive," Marguerite reassures her. "And no husband yet. Still, what is his name again?" She nods, forgets the name instantly, drinks quickly, licks her lips. "Fifty years ago," she begins, "my first husband and I arrived here, just like you. We lived just down there —" she points down the gentle slope that slides seaward: "A few houses, sunbaked fields, the occasional patch of conifers. We came six years after the war. From Holland." She considers Jo a moment or two, sets the glass down. "That's a story: he was in the Resistance. I nearly lost him more than once, and the two babies I had during the war both died — What can you say? It broke my heart, but I had to keep on working or the rest of the family would starve. I had two children already and the other four came afterwards. But all that time, while my husband was hiding from the Gestapo, I was a hairdresser. Cut, colour, perm — everyone wants it, even in a war. When peace came, I had a big salon in Rotterdam, eight stylists, someone to do the books. I made lots of money! But my poor husband was never happy. He was a cook, but he was always searching for something more in life … I said, let me teach you how to do the men's hair and then we can have two shops! But no, he wanted to open a hotel. That was his dream and he just had to try it. And of course, I could have a salon inside the hotel, for the guests. We heard of how it was here from a friend in the navy and we thought it could be the right place. I shipped all my furniture, the big heavy stuff from Holland, and all the equipment for a new salon, dryers, couches, massage tables, all brand new … I still have some of it. Beautiful. You must see sometime …

"The hotel didn't work out. So I opened a salon again, first in my house, then in town. It went well and my children grew up fine. But my first husband was never strong, poor man. He got sick … I decided to sell the business, so I could look after him. In the morning, I went to the lawyer to sign the papers, and that very same afternoon, he died! And the very next day after, my oldest came round. His wife had gone crazy and been locked up, so please would I look after the baby? Three weeks old. What can you do? I had her three years ... " Marguerite draws breath and Jo, frowning, struggles for something to say but Marguerite waves the attempt aside with a beringed hand.

"I helped my middle daughter set up her salon in Vancouver, and I did a certificate so I could run exercise classes ... I do believe that kept me young ... because when Mr Baker began courting me, I thought, no way, I'm sixty-four, I've got ten grandchildren, but I wanted to be kind because he was a sad man, a widower, living all alone in his so-big house. I could cheer him up with a bit of conversation ... We went for dinners, a little cruise up to Alaska. He was very respectful.

"'Enjoy yourself, Mum,' my kids told me ... He kept on asking me to marry him. But always I said *no*. Still, we went together to Mexico. This is what I am trying to get to: one day we were swimming back to the shore. I could swim faster than him and we agreed that I should go on ahead. After a while, I looked behind me and he was gone. I saw his bald head bob up for a second, then he was gone again, much longer this time. My heart began to pound ... "

Marguerite illustrates, banging her chest with the flat of her hand. "A heart attack, I thought, or cramps. I turned back and swam hard as I could. All the time, he kept disappearing. 'Hold on!' I shouted. But as I got close, I'm thinking, How on earth will I drag two hundred pounds of man back with me? I'm thinking, We're going to die here together, so I might as well have married you! Just as I arrived, he bobs up again ... "

Now Marguerite leans back in the plastic chair. She pauses, then opens her mouth, pulls her lips in and down over her teeth, pauses again.

"'I can't find them!' That's what he says! He's dropped his teeth and he's been trying to find them on the bottom!

"That made you laugh, eh? Well, the next time he asked me to marry him I said *yes*. We bought a waterbed, a time-share in

Mexico. We had eight years. Then, after he died I had an operation to my spine and they said I would never walk again, but I thought No Thanks! I do my exercises every morning to strengthen the muscles in my sides and stomach, and that way, I can keep myself up. So, here I am ... Welcome, dear. It's a lovely place to live. You will be happy here."

At this, they both look out: beyond the glass that runs two sides of the room, beyond the garden and the yellow-ochre fields is the sea, blue-green and spangled with sunlight. There's a complicated middle of wooded islands. A huge white cruise ship plies along the strait, far beyond it a distant mountain range, and floating above the rest, the huge snowcapped peak of Mount Baker, glowing violet-white.

Marguerite beams at the woman opposite, whose name she forgot some time back. She hopes she has cheered her up, though it's hard to tell. Again, she reaches out across the table and grasps her hand. "Thank God," she says, leaning back, suddenly tired. "Thank God, dear, that I took up hairdressing. It got me through everything."

A SAANICH THANKSGIVING

Stephen Hume

A papery sibilance ripples through ancient tree tops as though the whispers of lost grandmothers were announcing the arrival of WESELÁNEW, shaker of the leaves, striding once again into the country that most of us know as Saanich but that they would call WSÁNEĆ in the lovely syllables of their language.

The ghosts are only in my imagination, though. This faint rustling betrays an almost imperceptible breath of air, some late afternoon thermal effect. It goes sighing through the canopy above this old, old churchyard that rests in the farm fields along Mount Newton Cross Road, where I've come to meditate upon what is timeless and what is passing from the world.

Off to the west, glimpses of blue sea brocade the forest fringe like bits of lapis lazuli stitched into the hem of things, a fitting portent, perhaps. The gemstone was once favoured by Persian princes and Egyptian pharaohs for its ability to dispel melancholy and to impart wisdom. Lord knows, I feel a need for both as a thousand years dwindles with the season.

Beyond the mantle of evergreens and ocean, shadows already lengthen along the rumpled shoulders of mountains. They pool into a duskier hue along the lower slopes but melt from the high ridges in the rich, saffron light of a westering sun. A palpable serenity lingers on the afternoon. Then, as the breeze gathers strength on the temperature differential between sea and land, streamers of Spanish moss suddenly stir in the gnarled broadleaf maples. Perhaps the grandmothers are speaking after all. Now the willows, oaks and Lombardy poplars abruptly begin to snow their bronzed and golden leaves across the well-tended graves of William Thomson and his son Alexander. They go tumbling over the tomb of Aneas McPhail and swirl around the simple crosses erected for others now largely forgotten in the ebb of history. Some inscriptions in this churchyard are for people born during the Napoleonic Wars.

I've come to this tranquil little glade folded into the farm fields about twenty-five kilometres north of Victoria to mark for myself what will be the last Thanksgiving weekend of the bloodiest and most tumultuous century in human history. More than a hundred million slain in wars that laid waste to entire continents, wars spawning new wars, famine and pestilence stalking Africa while I, thanks to a lucky decision by immigrant parents, have spent my half of the century here in this oasis of peace and prosperity. And so, of all the possible vantage points from which to contemplate the bounty for which British Columbians should be grateful, the precinct of St Stephen's Anglican Church is for me among the best.

It is a place from which human experience spans our evolution from subsistence to agricultural plenty and from the Industrial Revolution to the post-industrial information economy. It has witnessed our great demographic shift from rural to urban existence. And yet it remains firmly anchored in the elemental world from which many of us are increasingly alienated by time and technology.

Templates are laid upon templates here. Not far south, on Little Saanich Mountain, scientists at the Dominion Astrophysical Observatory decipher signals from the farthest reaches of the universe and yet this small corner of calm feels like the centre of things, a place to ground all that. Just up the road is the long-occupied village site of W̲JOȽEȽP, the place of maple leaves. In the other direction, ȽÁU,WEL,N̲EW̲, the place of refuge where the Saanich people escaped from an earth-transforming flood, an event for which they still give thanks. And this little churchyard, I find, is a farmer's place for giving thanks, plain and unpretentious as a sweat-stained plough handle, founded just as the harvest was coming in one hundred thirty-seven years ago and still in use today, the oldest church in continuous service in all the province.

St Stephen's, in fact, is older even than Thanksgiving as most of us know it. Only in 1957 did Parliament formally establish the second Monday in October as "a day of General Thanksgiving to Almighty God for the bountiful harvest with which Canada has been blessed".

For all of Parliament's pompous annunciation of the holiday's recent roots in Christian doctrine, it's now largely a secular occasion that's easily embraced by almost everyone because the spiritual values it embodies are universal, extending well beyond the confines of creed.

Thanksgiving, of course, is far older than Christianity. It likely reaches back into the dawn of human consciousness, associated with seasonal rites of sympathetic magic intended to influence deities believed to control seasonal change that couldn't be explained outside the supernatural. Turn to Babylon or Greece, Abyssinia or Egypt, Imperial China or Imperial Rome, the great houses of the Coast Salish or the dynastic Maya and you will find some celebration of the earth's bounty. Among the Saanich people, the first salmon was greeted with an important ritual and then another ceremony marked the end of summer fishing that was signalled by the arrival of the dog salmon in Goldstream. The bales of dried fish and smoked clams, the boxes of berries and preserved eggs would all be stored for winter and thoughts would turn to the hunting of elk in the woodlands and the netting of ducks along the sloughs and ponds. A special ritual giving of food back to the fishing grounds celebrated this change of season.

Here in the northern hemisphere, Thanksgiving follows the fall equinox of late September, which to most of us on the south coast often seems more like a languid extension of summer, often still blessed by sun-drenched days and balmy evenings under brilliant stars. But by the second week of October there's no doubting anywhere in Canada, even here in the mild climate of the Saanich Peninsula, that the immense transition to winter which shapes us as a northern people has begun. For this holiday coincides with the seasonal tripping of two great switches in the natural world.

First, goes the light switch. As the length of the day decreases, signals are triggered in plants and animals that they must prepare for the hard months of winter that will soon arrive. Evidence of the power of this switch can be heard around wetlands, where frogs will suddenly erupt again with the calls we normally associate with April. That's because at this time of year the light balance is precisely the same as that of the spring equinox that tells them to wake up and get on with their sex lives. But as the light diminishes further, the frogs will soon subside again into the state of near-suspended animation that enables them to survive the cold months nestled in the insulating bottom mud.

Second, goes the temperature switch. As more time is spent turned away from the solar wind, the earth now radiates heat into space faster and for a longer time each day than it can absorb heat units delivered by rays from the sun which strike the earth's surface at an increasingly oblique angle.

In combination, these two switches instruct the trees to cut off their supply of water to the leaves, the miraculous little factories where photosynthesis converts sunlight to stored energy for the plant's use. Sap retreats into the roots, below the range at which frost can penetrate into the ground. Above the surface, the dry tree is better able to endure freezing temperatures and thus avoid the rupturing of cells caused by the expansion of internal ice crystals.

Deprived of water, the process of photosynthesis ends and chlorophyll, the vivid green compound within the leaves that actually converts light and air to food for the plant, begins to dissipate. Now we get our splendid seasonal evidence that autumn has arrived as all the deciduous leaves change colour to the copper, bronze and golden hues like those that rustle and whisper above St Stephen's and its shadowy churchyard.

What we are seeing as autumn advances is the shape of things as they are. All the gaudy excess of summer has been stripped away. The flare of fall colours through the tree tops is really the gradual disclosure of the leaves in their true form, no longer masked by the universal green camouflage of their chlorophyll. These colours also reveal a bit of the biochemistry of each tree species.

The brilliant yellow of aspens signals the presence of carotin, the compound that colours carrots and egg yolks. A soluble sugar named anthocyanin colours certain other species' leaves according to how acid or alkaline the sap has been: more acidic trees flame red, more alkaline tend toward the purple.

Walk through these woods on a sunny afternoon in early fall and in some places one can't help but notice that the air seems filled with shimmering gossamer. For some reason that nobody fully understands, at this time of year countless tiny spiders will point their spinnerets skyward, shoot strands of silk into the air and let the breeze carry them off, sometimes for miles — another seasonal mystery to be contemplated on any fall stroll through the rolling Saanich countryside.

Of course, autumn is a season long associated in literature and art with an ironic mystery. Successive generations of painters and poets have meditated upon the way in which the richest abundance in life precedes the threadbare austerity of death. From the spare syllables of the monk Ryozen writing near Kyoto almost a thousand years ago to the lush images of John Keats' "season of mists and mellow fruitfulness" in an English countryside the Saanich Peninsula evokes, the juxtaposition of autumnal fullness with the skull behind it has fascinated writers and readers around the world. And for such melancholy thoughts, there's no better metaphor than the distinctive fall eruption of the ghost pipes and the witches' butter that seem entirely in keeping with Halloween rites that are just around the corner.

Fall is the time of fungi. The lethal red and white of fly agaric and pale hue of death caps burst from the soil along with more benign fungi like morels, chanterelles and puffballs. All these fungi, colourful or not, are intimates of death, living as they do upon decaying organic matter — which is in great abundance when the leaves fall and the seasonal rains return.

Yet these companions of the dead are essential to the renewal of life. Fungi break complex organic compounds into the simple carbon, nitrogen, potassium and phosphorus which can be easily absorbed by plants and will be vital during the explosion of growth which will come again next spring. So the fairy rings in the lawn and the toadstools in the woods are all evidence of the eternal equilibrium of life and death, abundance and scarcity, the miraculous waxing and waning of the physical as well as the spiritual world that we celebrate each Thanksgiving.

This particular celebration is no more noteworthy to the natural world because it happens to be the last one of the millennium and yet it remains compelling in the human psyche because of our obsession with round numbers. It marks the four hundred and twenty-first year since the first such celebration is known to have been held by European newcomers to North America. However, that first Thanksgiving was not celebrated by the Puritan pilgrims to New England, as American myth-making would have us believe. The first in the historic record was held by the English maritime explorer Sir Martin Frobisher on the rocky shores of Baffin Island in what is now Nunavut in the year 1578.

Here on the Saanich Peninsula, I am as far from the Arctic in geography and climate as this Thanksgiving is in time from the

Elizabethan era. And yet some things don't change. Inside the small wooden church of St Stephen's, a rainbow of light streams through the stained glass window above the altar and floods across age-blackened pews as it must have done in Frobisher's time, helping no doubt to further fade the hand-lettered scrolls which list Saanich boys who now leaven the farm fields of Flanders and Normandy and the Scheldt, ten thousand miles from home.

The image that graces the window is charming in its gentle humour, an infant Jesus in his mother's arms as barnyard animals in the background look wisely down upon the human flock gathered below. At the entrance, the lectern is a Coast Salish eagle balanced on the tail of a diving killer whale, an invitation to the fusion of cultures that characterize this place — tolerance, one of the other less tangible but no less valuable bounties of life in British Columbia.

Outside, around gleaming white clapboard, the timeless fields of abundance roll away in all directions. There are beehives just across the fence. The faint lowing of cattle drifts up the valley. The huge barn of Woodwyn Farm is a thumbnail in the distance. The holly trees that skirt the gravel road are vivid with crimson berries. And all along the rural approaches, roadside stands offer pumpkins, preserves, cut flowers, pears and apples and the first of the sumptuous winter squash.

For most visitors to or from the continent, the lovely landscape of the peninsula whizzes by in the narrow highway corridor between the Swartz Bay terminal and dinner at The Empress or on the ferry. But wander the side roads and it is quickly apparent that of all the 2.4 million hectares of farmland in BC, this verdant 250-square-kilometre wedge that juts thirty rich kilometres into the sea must be among the most striking.

To be sure, there are more productive fields in the Fraser Valley and vaster fields in the Peace River district on the other side of the Rockies. There are more dramatic places in the arid grasslands of the interior and richer soils on the mountain-bound flood plains of the Cascades and the Monashees. For beauty and diversity, however, few places match the small holdings of the little northward extension of what Sir James Douglas described as "this perfect Eden" when he came ashore to establish Fort Victoria for the Hudson's Bay Company and thus ensured the binding of Vancouver Island to what would later become Canada.

Why a "perfect Eden"?

Partly it's the mild climate, drier and warmer than the lower mainland with its walls of mountains, Arctic outflows and adjacent snowpacks and glaciers. Sheltered from the hurricane fury of the Pacific by a mountain spine, the southeast corner of Vancouver Island basks in a semi-arid Mediterranean climate that permits cactus to grow on the adjacent Gulf Islands and flowers to bloom in every winter month on the peninsula.

Partly it's the terrain itself, this gorgeous, rolling meadowland of hayfields and hedgerows, punctuated by forest groves and fields of flowers, fertile bottoms and rocky outcrops with spectacular glimpses of the sea through garry oaks and the exotic tangle of arbutus trees.

Partly it's simply the weight of history because as an overlay on the Saanich territory, this is the oldest fully cultivated region in the Pacific province and therefore ranks as the oldest continuously occupied farm community west of almost everything but the Selkirk Settlement in Manitoba.

St Stephen's, for example, was founded in 1862 on five acres of farmland deeded to the Anglican diocese by the same William Thomson who now sleeps in the churchyard — even though he was a steadfast Presbyterian. It was consecrated by Bishop George Hills, who noted thoughtfully in his diary that "among those present were three Jews who gave liberally and took a marked interest in the proceedings".

The Christians of the south island contributed to the building of the first synagogue in western Canada. Some of the original homesteaders were free blacks from the United States who came north rejecting a country that still tolerated slavery. Their children attended school with those of white settlers and Metis voyageurs. Today, St Stephen's operates in a covenant with the Roman Catholic parish, sharing congregations and conducting integrated services at Easter — another intersection of cultures and beliefs in a spirit of tolerance and generosity that celebrates the diversity and difference for which most of us are thankful. Even from its earliest origins, this little church precinct in rural Saanich resonates with the underlying spirit of Thanksgiving.

Two huge Douglas firs flank the front door of the church. These trees were planted by Thomson when St Stephen's was built, perhaps a kind of homage to his own deliverance. He had come ashore in a December gale in 1853 when the American brigantine *William* was wrecked at Clo-oose on the wild outer coast that is still known as the Graveyard of the Pacific. Along with the fifteen other survivors, Thomson was enslaved for six months by the fierce Nitinat who ruled that stretch of shoreline. The Hudson's Bay Company factor at Fort Victoria purchased the captives' freedom with a bale of blankets.

Later Thomson settled on a quarter section of land near Aneas McPhail, said to be the first white settler in the territory, although McPhail himself disagreed that he was. He'd heard from his Saanich Indian neighbours that a white man had lived peacefully on his place in the time of the grandfathers.

Thomson later identified a clearing where a cabin had long since decayed and there he found a Spanish halberd. Whose weapon might it have been? Did it belong to some shipwrecked sailor making his way east from the inhospitable west coast? Major George Nicholson says an unidentified sailing ship — so old that even as early as 1880 the Nuu-chah-nulth had no knowledge of it — lay partially buried in the sands of Long Beach until a spring storm covered it for good just before the Great War. Was the halberd left with a man marooned by the Spanish navy, as it was wont to do for formal punishment? Could it have belonged to a survivor who had made his way to the sea from the legendary Spanish army column that stories from the interior say was lost while exploring northward from California, some say ambushed and massacred in or near the Similkameen Valley? Was it an item that followed aboriginal trade routes? Or just a souvenir from the undeclared naval war between the English and the Spanish in the New World that was packed into the country and left behind when its European owner died?

Whatever the origins, all that now remains of that initial clearing is the poignant splinter of an enigma, as elusive in its own way as our understanding of the deep paradox we celebrate at Thanksgiving, where abundance is the herald of hardship and the dying of one generation portends the birth of another.

About Alexander Thomson, who lies next to his father, there is no mystery, however. He was the first non-native child born in the region in 1859, the harbinger of a rising tide of settlement. Today more than fifty farms can be found within twenty minutes' drive of St Stephen's and those first homesteads. Their produce is astonishingly diverse. There is thick wild flower honey from the apiaries of Babe's, whose customers drive up from the United States to buy their winter stock. There are kiwi fruit and Adriatic figs, lingonberries and quinces — an ancient fruit the Greeks thought divine and a bit of an aphrodisiac to boot — although a dish of fresh-picked strawberries and cream from a local dairy is said to work the same magic.

One farm specializes in cucumbers of all varieties. Another lets customers choose between different kinds of garlic, Korean or Chinese, Italian or Spanish, even Quebec or Ontario varieties. There are fresh free-range eggs to be had down one lane and fresh-baked bread to be had down another. Some vendors are found only by serendipitous chance, others by long-established reputation.

Among the best known is Le Coteau Farm on Oldfield Road, famous with parents for its nursery, with cooks for the quality of its produce and with children for its annual Pumpkin Fest and corn maze, complete with a suitably gruesome Haunted House staffed by enthusiastic teenagers. On the other side of the peninsula, overlooking Haro Strait and a distant Mount Baker that seems to hang suspended in the sky like a snow-clad apparition, is the equally well-known Michell Brothers Farm, itself one of the oldest establishments in the region and justly praised for its kitchen produce. There are farms with names like Silver Rill and Windy Hill, there are berry farms, dairy farms and daffodil ranches. Other farms of lesser renown sprawl along the byways from Bear Hill to Land's End and many sell their produce on summer Saturdays from booths at the Peninsula Country Market on the Saanich Fair grounds.

The annual fall fair has been going almost as long as St Stephen's. It began when the farmers who had founded the church met in 1868 to show their produce and livestock and have some harvest fun. Today it's still one of the most important — and oldest — agricultural fairs in western Canada. But on this weekend, with the Saanich Fair laid to rest for another year and the century sliding toward an oblivion as inevitable as my own, I visit the modest retreat of Apple Press Farm, where Joan Byers and Virginia Porter have grafted forty-two varieties of heritage apples onto one thousand two hundred trees. At their orchard one might buy Ashmead's Kernel, an apple right out of 1700 Gloucestershire, or the Astrachan Red, from the Russia of Tolstoy's *War and Peace*, or a Lady, grown in Louis XIII's gardens at Orleans in 1628, or a Kindal Sinap from Asia Minor, or an Esopus Spitzenburg, said to be a favorite of Thomas Jefferson, framer of the American Declaration of Independence.

At Apple Press, principle takes precedence over marketing. There's no cold storage. The fruit is sold fresh and only when it's ready. The crop sells out each fall, with customers contracting orders well in advance.

"Our philosophy is not to pick fruit before it is ripe. We let it ripen only on the tree. Each year we do an apple-tasting week around Thanksgiving. Once customers taste an apple, we've sold it," Joan tells me.

Not surprisingly, perhaps, there's a booming trade in gift boxes. For ten dollars the farm will prepare one with nine different heritage varieties of apple. But this end of the century Thanksgiving the harvest is running five weeks late because of the cool, wet spring, Joan says, and while the yield looks good, the apples will be smaller than usual. Right now, only varieties that normally ripen in August are available. But she's not worried. Her customers come when their favourite apple is ready, not the other way round.

Indeed, already clients are lining up to order an apple known as Bramley Seedling, a variety from Nottinghamshire that dates from the time of Lord Nelson and the Battle of Trafalgar. It is a variety prized by chefs for its baking properties — it cooks into a pale, rich, creamy fluff, as fleeting on the palate as its time on the market shelf. Which raises the question of whether Apple Press itself will be there when I next return. There are no guarantees.

It's in the nature of things for these small farms and their markets to come and go as the economy dictates and owners change, so every expedition in search of peaches-and-cream corn or the perfect tomato or just the right butternut squash or bumbleberry pie is a bittersweet encounter with the mingled joys and sorrows of the season, with the equilibrium of abundance and loss that in the central metaphor of the event.

Around the corner and up the lane a wanderer would once have found the wealth of autumn accumulating at the Deep Cove Farmer's Market, housed in a weathered barn. Among the mounds of scallopini squash and sweet Hungarian peppers were pumpkin pies and fresh baked bread from local kitchens. There was salal berry jelly, plum rum conserve and Best Ever Beets, "picked, packed and pickled" in North Saanich. Kids were invited to crush their own apples in an antique press and then drink the sweet soft cider, or to ride a wagon out to the pumpkin patch and choose their own jack-o'-lantern, or to get lost in a maze made from baled hay.

Those small pleasures, some now swept away in the river of time that eventually carries off everything, are only a glimpse of the astonishing productivity of British Columbia's more than twenty thousand farms. Each year, working from less than four per cent of the province's land base, they bring to market two hundred commodities worth close to two billion dollars at home and in over a hundred countries worldwide. Processing this food generates another 1.4 billion dollars in the provincial economy.

One way to think about this remarkable achievement is to consider the province's land area as a football field. Start at one goal line. All that wealth — and what riches have greater value than food on the table? — is generated from the first three yards of the field.

But Thanksgiving is not only a celebration of prosperity, as the quiet outlook from St Stephen's reminds us. It's also a celebration of sharing.

Just up the road at Don and Lorraine Smyth's market garden, the sunflowers have begun to droop and the berry canes are touched with bronze but the roadside stand has been turned over to Save the Children Canada for a Thanksgiving fund raiser.

I found a chatty Patsy McAvity bagging fresh cranberries. For a two-cup bag, a two-dollar donation was requested. There were Anjou pears and red crab apples and flower bulbs from the gardens at Beacon Hill Park in Victoria.

"People bring us the surplus produce from their gardens," Patsy explained. "Isn't it great? My husband doesn't like the fall when the leaves go and the trees are bare, but I love it. I love this time of year with all its bounty. We have a couple of squirrels. They have just been frantic helping harvest our walnuts, but they're just like us, aren't they — we're all taking up the harvest and putting our gardens to bed, getting ready for the quiet season."

She stops to listen a moment to the peeping of tree frogs that greets a sudden shower.

"I haven't heard them for a long time. It's lovely, isn't it?"

No more lovely, though, than her own Thanksgiving task, standing in a drizzle that still has the softness of summer but hints of the hard sleets to come, offering the gifts of local farmers to raise money for needy kids that none of them will likely ever know or meet.

This, too, is a reminder of the eternal question with which the quiet churchyard at St Stephen's rings. What is it, really, for which we give thanks?

Not for our material comforts. Not for the accumulation of wealth and possessions. Not even, perhaps, for the groaning tables of a festive dinner surrounded by family. No, it's simpler than that. It's for the gift of living where we still have an opportunity to fashion a better world, one where we may yet learn to love one another, to help one another without reference to who we are or where we come from, to admire and celebrate one another's differences across cultures and creeds, as the founders of this little country church once did so long ago.

Perhaps what this last Saanich Thanksgiving of the millennium really celebrates is not a particular event in history, or even a particular place in time, but our collective understanding that the power of redemption lies both with us and within us — and our gratitude is mostly for the opportunity to use it wisely and well.

THE GIFT

Susan Musgrave

I used to be paranoid. Last week, for instance, when my signal lights weren't working and I found myself trailing a squad card to Sidney, I convinced myself that the police were actually following *me*. I had to lose them. I slowed until they were out of sight, then took an alternative route to my doctor's office.

My doctor said that paranoia, like jealousy, was simply another form of intuition. I'd been gifted with strong intuitions, I knew, and drove straight to SOS to get my indicators fixed.

Late Sunday afternoon I sent my husband and daughter to Sidney for boneless chicken breasts. Really, it was an excuse — I wanted some time alone. It was raining; I told them to drive carefully and not to hurry back. Five minutes after they'd left I was standing at the window, waiting for them to return.

It seemed to be raining harder. The road looked slick; would the tires grip? I set to work making the Chocolate Chip Surprises I'd been promising all weekend.

I had the first batch in the oven when I heard the siren. Racing to the window, I saw a police car making a U-turn right in front of our house. He sped off, lights flashing, toward town.

My family had been gone for thirty-five minutes. It didn't take that long to buy boneless chicken breasts at Thrifty's, unless of course Thrifty's didn't have any and they'd had to go further afield, to Safeway, for example. I'd decided I'd give them another ten minutes before I really started worrying, when a fire truck streaked past, followed by an ambulance.

If you want peace, prepare for war — that's my motto. At once I imagined my car, with the two people I loved more than life itself, trapped inside. How soon would anybody notify me? If the glove compartment had been spared, someone would find registration papers, and even though my address had changed and I hadn't bothered to inform Motor Vehicles, I still had the same telephone number.

Four fifty-five. I checked my cookies and went to wait by the telephone. I'd never realized how lonely an empty booster seat could look on a chair, or a pair of trousers with the top button missing. My husband had been asking me for months to sew that button on, "When you have a moment."

Living alone, I'd have moments. No, I thought, I would take my own life rather than live on without my family. I would hurl myself off the cliff that very evening.

The cliff was across the road. But when I looked I saw that the tide was unusually low. I saw a family clamming at the water's edge. If I were to kill myself tonight I would have to hurl myself off the mud flats and spoil that family's outing.

Five o'clock. Maybe the police wouldn't phone, but would send someone personally, in which case they would go to the wrong address. Oh, why hadn't I informed Motor Vehicles when I moved? Rather than wait the days it would probably take for them to track me down, I decided to take the plunge. It took a lot of guts to call the RCMP and ask, "Have there been any casualties in the Safeway parking lot this evening?"

"No accidents," the Colwood detachment, which is what you get when you call the police in Sidney, informed me. "At least none that have been reported."

None that have been reported. I hung up, no happier than before, and stared at the treacherous road. I should have had my tires rotated, I just knew it. My mechanic had called me a worry-wart the last time, so I hadn't wanted to mention it.

"I have suffered a great many catastrophes in my life," Mark Twain wrote. "Most of them have never happened." I was trying to convince myself that nothing might happen this time, either, that it was simply "another form of intuition" taking hold of my better judgment, when the brown Accord slowed and pulled into the drive. My husband and daughter emerged, alive. "Something's burning," my daughter said, as she came bounding through the front door laden with packages.

I took the charred Surprises out of the oven and put the frozen chicken wings — all they'd been able to get — in the sink to thaw. My husband had bought a record, one he'd wanted for Christmas, and I listened to a cut called "Mothers of the Disappeared" while my daughter told me they'd been all over Sidney trying to find something to cheer me up. But it wasn't until I broke open the box of small heart-shaped chocolates she'd bought in a post-Valentine's sale that I burst into tears properly.

"See," said my daughter, looking knowingly at my husband, "I told you I knew how to make her happy."

THE POND HUNTERS

Charlotte Biscay

ONE thing his wife could say about him was that George Mathers was puzzlingly fastidious about maps. He insisted that they be folded correctly, tucking the edges into the creases, so that they opened up like flowers, or accordions, whenever there was need to consult them again. He did it with such precision, and she, the neat one, the one who was forever fluffing pillows, could never get it right. The last fold was somehow always the opposite of what it should be, leaving the map lumpy and misshapen. And then he would scowl and grab it and fold it the proper way. It was totally out of keeping with everything else she knew about him, and after the better part of a lifetime she knew him well enough. But there was a side to him, the map side, that predated their long union, and hinted of something, something determined, something that came from a maddeningly unknowable past.

To know was to possess, so perhaps she was simply grieving for what she could never have. Whenever she tried to imagine him then, a person separate from her, an imperiously curious child, say, in the bombed-out Chelsea house, or later, playing a jazz piano in one of those smoky pubs, or scaling the side of some craggy Welsh mountain, the images would evaporate almost as soon as she could conjure them.

They were driving, George at the wheel, Giselle navigating, along Old West Saanich Road. She preferred West Saanich to the highway, old or new the route never failed to please her, a sun-dappled passage through cedars, hemlocks and alders that rose, protectively, on either side of them. Shaggy trees, not wild exactly, but unkempt. The hemlock especially. They looked tipsy, unsteady, charming, like big men who'd drunk too much, trying to get a foothold on the forest floor. What was left of it, anyhow.

"Can't you see it?"

"Of course. Yes. No, wait. Slow down. I had it only a minute ago." She had the map in her lap and was trying to reorient herself while George charged on.

"You have the thing upside down."

"No I don't." She looked again. "Well, yes, maybe I do. I've never been good at this."

"Don't you think it's about time?"

She laughed. For all his faults she could never stay angry with him for long. From the start she had been won over by his kindness. And she'd been right: at bottom he was a kindly man. Serious, opinionated, but kind, and that was what mattered above all else. Arguments, yes, but nothing mean. No hitting below the belt. You had to be able to tell. The trick was in the telling. What he'd be like in seven, twenty, forty, maybe even fifty years.

When they'd first met she thought she'd never get used to his politeness. "You are so *reck*," she'd said. It was amazing. They were pedestrians then, trying to negotiate Piccadilly Circus, and he'd steered her away from the oncoming traffic when she, an intrepid Parisian, had tried to cross without the light. He was the Londoner, through and through, proper and gentle, and she was the reckless one. She'd even had to persuade him to do some rather unusual things in bed. Then he went off to Greenland, and she went back to the ballet in Paris, and when, a few years later, he came to see her again, he was changed.

There was a roughness about him, a recklessness even. He had grown a beard, shaggy and reddish, when the thick hair on his head was almost black. But stranger still were the eyes. There was a look in them, a light. It was as though he'd had a vision, or, contrarily, that the snow had blinded him. And there was something about the colour of his irises: one as green as a river, the other as blue as ice. How could it have been that she had never noticed that before?

He reached across to tap the edge of the map. "Bearhole, it's called."

She studied his face in profile for a second, then, looking down in her lap, traced the blue line for Old West Saanich, keeping an eye on either side of it. She kept moving her finger until it went past the crease. Then she had to fold the map in half.

"It's only tiny," he said.

At last! A road no more than a kilometre, if that, to the left. They could easily miss it, the way he was driving. Not for the first time that morning, she begged him to slow down.

"They must have caught a bear there once."

"Turn!"

The pick-up spun on its wheels and with an alarming swish was on Bearhole Road, its tail end wagging. Scarcely a road — the truck almost filled the width of it — and after a short way it wasn't even sealed. Not the sort normally marked on a map, but George always used good maps, the most detailed he could find. There was a story in that, and the picture of a younger George poring over charts in the government map office sprang into Giselle's mind, but the office wasn't there anymore, and the ruts in the road soon brought her back to the present. The light was dim because of the trees and the sky, what she could see of it through the overhanging branches, had turned a pearly grey, with wisps of noon sunlight in it. They came to a small bend and there, on the right, peeking through the tangle of wild roses, was a gate in a rusted wire fence, and beyond it, the pond.

George hopped out and after a moment Giselle followed. By the time she got there he was leaning on the gate and grinning.

"I knew it was here." She could barely see it through the columns of reeds, but, yes, now and then, she caught the glint of pale sunlight on water; the rest of the pond was covered with the broad flat pea-green leaves of lilies. "I'm going to get my rod," he said.

He wanted her to come but she declined. "I'm tired," she said. She watched nervously from the truck as he opened the gate and trudged off through the reeds towards the pond until he was gone from sight. Although she believed absolutely in the rightness of his mission she was always edgy about it. She looked around. Everything seemed so quiet, unnaturally so, which was a little ironic, since it was this scene that was "natural", and the things and the places she was used to and comfortable in were not. She pulled a book from her bag and settled into reading.

A minute or so later, a car squeezed past her on the road. Trying to pretend she belonged there she waved a cheery hello. She left the book open but didn't resume her reading. There was a motor running, coming from the left. She looked, and was chagrined to see a woman puttering in her garden and, up a slight incline, a man with a mower. He pushed it relentlessly, as though he wasn't quite convinced of the necessity, and when he came to the edge of the grass, swung it around to attack the next part. The grass was quite long and thick, but the garden was lovely. A lovely scene, but she wished with all her heart she wasn't there. They could be mortifying, these forays.

The woman in the garden went on with her puttering, the man with his mowing, and Giselle picked up her book again and tried to read. It was a library book, a thriller, set in post-Soviet Moscow. Anything about Russia fascinated her, and it titillated her that they were so close to it, and yet so far. And she loved the feel of library books, the coating they put on the covers, the slickness of them in her fingers, the contrast to the soft, aging pages inside. When she was still dancing her company had gone to Moscow and performed at the Bolshoi. She savoured the memory still. The movement, the colour. The beautiful gentleness of the Russian speech, the angular Cyrillic. This was just a thriller, no great shakes as literature, but it didn't matter, it took her back. She had been a good dancer, but she hadn't the dedication, for a dancer she hadn't been disciplined, hadn't been *reck* enough.

Suddenly, George's face appeared in the truck window. He was panting slightly, and exhilarated as he always was when trudging through the bush.

"Did you catch anything?"

"No, but the fish are there. There's just the right level of calcium carbonate. And there's another one, up the hill, not on the map. I've been talking to the woman who owns it. She'd like to meet you, she runs a kind of music school." He tilted his head in the direction of the garden.

Giselle slipped her book in her bag and climbed down from the truck. As they came closer she realised that neither the garden, nor the woman, nor the man with the mower were anything like what they had seemed. The woman was smiling. She had a strong, round, peasant-like face, and wispy grey hair she wore in a loose bun. The man, in his twenties, had a thin beard and was dressed something like a ballet Cossack. A son? He didn't seem a son. But from the way the woman responded to him, speaking to him about the garden, the mowing, Giselle gathered that he lived there.

"Julia," the woman said, offering her hand. "Julia Meyer. Your husband was saying you're a dancer."

Giselle reddened and laughed. "Well, some time ago."

The house was one of those very few in the area that appeared to grow from the bush around it, almost indistinguishable from the trees. Julia led them through a shambles of a kitchen into the main room, the meeting room, she called it. Giselle looked up at the high-pitched timber ceiling and the rafters below. The interior would have been lush and dark, a forest itself, were it not for the large windows that let in great slabs of light. There was an upright piano against one wall, its front panel intricately carved, and on another hung an old oblong tapestry depicting a medieval village.

Julia offered them tea, which they both refused, asking for water instead.

Returning from the kitchen with two glasses, she gave them to her guests and sat down on a stool herself, wiping her hands on her shorts.

"Your husband was telling me about the pond. I found it fascinating," she said. "Just fascinating. About its stillness, so the fish don't all point in the same direction, waiting for the food to come to them. They have to go looking for it, they have to move around. So I told him that we had a visitor here once, he ran a class for us, to show us how water responds to sound. He's done this all over the world. And he took pictures of the pond, and I wanted to show you." Her hands on her knees, she levered herself up from the stool and disappeared again into another room.

"What did you tell her?" Giselle whispered.

George shrugged. "That I was interested in the pond. What else would I tell her?"

"That you were fishing. On her property."

"It isn't her property. It belongs to a neighbour."

Giselle rolled her eyes upward, to the vaulted timber roof.

"But there's another one, like I said, a bigger one, and she said I could come anytime." He would have gone on about it but Julia had returned and was positioning the stool between them. When she was satisfied that they were precisely equidistant from her, she opened the book in her hands and spread it across her knees.

It was an oddly shaped book, short but wide. Smoothing the glossy pages, Julia launched into an expansive dissertation, about the man who had come to visit, about his life's purpose, and the photographs he had taken. The first, she explained, was of a lake in Los Angeles, his native city, and depicted the cacophonous jangle of its traffic and its effect on the water. The picture was an angry design of swirling reds and blues, mimicking to perfection the jagged swerves of neon.

"Ezio had this theory, like I said, that water reacts to sounds, and their effects on it could be recorded, not just in sound, as you would expect, but in images. And he's convinced that there are beneficial sounds, the ones that make the water tranquil and pure, and polluting sounds, and the patterns from them are discordant and disturbing. Look, here's one of 'Clair de Lune'."

Giselle and George stretched their necks to get the best view of the pictures, George from a slip-covered armchair, Giselle from a low horsehair sofa. Their skill at polite conversation was strained as well — for years they had been a self-contained couple, whose claims on each other made up the major, and most satisfactory, discourse in their lives, for all the contradictions between them. But here was a pattern as harmonious as the first one was jumpy and abstracted, aglow with translucent, intersecting circles of blue and green and rose, and it gave them something to say. "Like a Monet painting," Giselle breathed with delight. And it was true, the luminous pastel hues were pale but vivid, their shapely arcs whispered contentment, and wholeness. "Everything is as I'd imagined, if I could have imagined it," George added.

And Julia took note of their wonder with the kind of smile she might beam if she had taken the photograph herself, the kind commonly reserved for scenic vacation views or pictures of doted-upon grandchildren.

But as she turned the pages the images grew gradually dark again. It was as though that one glimpse of harmony was enough, all she was willing to dispense. A parade of lurid chartreuses, browns and murky lemons left both George and Giselle speechless, and Giselle, only a minute earlier suffused with pure pleasure, was gripped by an urge to escape. She felt the aggressiveness in Julia, in spite of her friendliness, possibly even due to it. There was an aggression to certain kinds of sociability, a challenge, unspoken, unacknowledged, but there. *Hell is other people*, George was fond of intoning, though he too, when called upon, could be as amiable and gregarious as the next.

They came to the last page, a monstrous Rorschach splotch of reds and black. "An argument," said Julia. "Ezio calls it war. And it is war, a conflict between two people. The sound rising, shouts, names. If that can do this, imagine what a full-scale war must do. The effect on our water."

Giselle glanced around the room again, as though she could hear the arguments. Yes, she could hear them, the yelling, the door slams, more than any music, she was sure. And the mower had started up again, raucous, insistent, or perhaps had been in the background all the time, and the scene outside shimmered in her head: the youth with the wispy beard, the Cossack trousers, lunging at the grass with it, an enemy to coerce, conquer, subdue — or the stand-in for an enemy.

The afternoon had drained away. The sun was casting pale elongated shadows. George had his heart set on more investigation, Giselle would rather have called it a day. All the same, she might as well give herself up to it. A pond-hunting day. The whole of it. Why not? A pond off Haldon Road turned out to be three ponds, two of which hadn't made George's map. Didn't matter: a large new house with a fence blocked all three of them off. But further on a chain of them began on Wallace Road, dots of blue across a golden field, bound on all sides by yards.

The pick-up swerved and churned up the dust as George lurched from one possibility to another, and was stymied at each in turn. Fences and hedges bedevilled him. Then they found one at the end of a road behind the racetrack, hidden by a row of blackberry bushes. George reached for his rod, got out, slammed the cab door, and disappeared in the blackberries. Giselle took her book from her bag. A character speaks: *You say Moscow is a scary town. Why? Because there's no tradition of private property in Russia* ... And her mind drifted to the cafeteria at the hostel where she had stayed, member of the proletarian chorus. The twisted spoons, the chipped cups on her tray. And how they had argued about that, when he came back from Greenland. Admiring her for going, for putting herself, as he'd said, on the line, and her saying no, it was nothing like that, it was the movement, the colour, the genuine love the Russians had for art. Yet she saw even there that something was wrong: art reserved only for art, beauty for the stage or page, denying it to a cup or spoon. The allocation of scarce resources, he had shrugged, her scientist with a beard. But though the words had been hard and precise, there were those eyes, transformed.

Just then she felt his shadow at the door, heard it open and was greeted with an unexpected smile. "Nice one," he said. "I found a really nice one." She smelled water and the faintly sour smell of vegetation as he slid his bulk onto the seat. "Met the owner, too." Giselle made no reply. "He's from England, not far from Barking, would you believe."

"Thank God for that."

He turned the key in the ignition and backed down the lane a way before slipping into the driveway and spinning in the right direction. She listened to the gravel bounce against the bottom of the truck. She found that she was pleased, and the fact of it pleased. Two ponds in a day, not a bad score.

"Ready for home?"

"One more to check," he said.

There was a road, then another, then another rutted lane. At the end of it was a quarry, surrounded by a chain-link fence. The sky was dramatic now, shot with the colours of sunset. Almost worth being there, for the sky. She had heard a man say once that the colours on the coast were cool, that the water in the air somehow leached them of warmth, of light, but she found when she scanned them herself that it wasn't quite true. There was warmth in the sky. Reds shading into mauve. Not quite a desert sky, but not a Baltic one either.

He got out of the car and this time she followed. Together they strolled to the edge of the quarry. A large metal quonset hut loomed dark against her sky. Looping their fingers in the links, they rested a moment against the fence.

The men had left for the day and the machinery, giant bulldozers and rock-choppers, stood mute and sad, gentle monsters awaiting the morning and their masters. She was taken by their lumbering beauty. "Concrete," George said. "They're making concrete." He sighed. "Let's go back."

But then they saw that the road didn't end just there but continued as a dirt trail from the quarry past a cluster of farm buildings straight into the bush. As George manoeuvred the truck Giselle kept her eye open for a clearing, for any sign of water. And there, with the low-lying sun glinting off its surface, suffusing it with soft hues of gold and rose, was the largest, most beautiful pond she had seen that day. She turned to her husband and grinned. It was as though the gods had been kind, rewarding them for their efforts of the day. She believed in those things, gods and spirits, she did, and though she laughed at herself and George often scoffed, she knew in her heart that he relied on her to, as he was unable to believe in them himself. And this time she opened her door at the very same moment as he did and together they walked between the pliant saplings and through the long faintly crackling grass to the water, golden and still in the waning light. Silly long-winged insects were skimming along the surface between the lilies and she smiled that closed-mouth smile of hers remembering that chorus she'd danced in so many years ago. Here and there was a circlet of rings where a fish was rising, and as she watched George send the line from his reel shimmying over the water, and saw his iron dun touch down, she marvelled at his persistence, marvelled that they could find such a place in the centre of a city; well, not exactly a city as they'd known them, but a blanket of farms and suburbs, *banlieus* as she'd call them once, flung across the land, but different from the land, this pond, these trees.

She squatted to scoop up some of the water and let it trickle through her fingers. It smelled of frogs and the faint click of insects sounded in her ears. George was casting again. She heard it without looking up, the hum of the line as it spun from the reel. She wondered if he would catch one and what he would catch if he did. The sun flared on the horizon, a flickering band of light just before sinking, shooting shadows and long trails of colour onto the water. And then the sky went darker, a moist, powdery darkness and the air went cool. The best time of day, always. The changing hour, a time of communion, of almost mystical shadows. And then she sensed another sort of shadow and turned and saw what she saw, blocking off what little remained of the sun. "George," she whispered.

It was a woman, in silhouette, on a horse. Slowly, as Giselle's eyes adjusted, the rider's features emerged. The woman was dressed in jeans, a shirt and long black riding boots. Her face was tanned and smooth, a young face, unformed.

The animal shook its head and snorted as the rider slid off and started striding towards them through the grass. "Hey," she called. "What are you doing?"

Giselle closed her eyes, listening to the water splashing as George waded through the pond. Then she eased them open and rose from her squatting position to face the rider. For all her reticence Giselle was no coward. Before George was able to reach them she shouted back, "Quiet, please. My husband is fishing!" No matter that they were quite mad to be there, that she was making a hell of a racket herself — her reckless self had come back. The one that had danced in a forbidden country and dashed headlong into London's chaotic traffic.

"Your husband can't fish here. This is a private farm."

Giselle took a quick glance around. "What are you farming? I can't see any fields." In any case, what difference would it make? In England, in France … in Russia even … Giselle rifled through her mind for arguments. But the woman was implacable, all that far outside her ken.

"You're quarrying, that's what you're doing," said a dripping George.

"Look, I only work here …"

"So who's your boss?"

"There's a sign on the road."

"We didn't come that way. We came through the back."

"I really don't see how."

"No," said George. "You bloody well wouldn't."

"Come George, let's go."

The rider remounted as they got back into the truck. Giselle twisted round and watched her through the rear window. A silhouette again, looming in the fading light, watching them go. The pick-up bounced along the gravel until they came to Wain Road, and there, sure enough, at the entrance, was the sign. A farm, a quarry? No, it was to be a resort.

They didn't need the map now; they were heading home. She set it aside, unfolded, and considered the day. The road, their stops, the water. She thought about the pond, that last one, and how it would appear through the lens of Ezio's camera, a snarl of bellicose black and reds. She had never felt so angry, not in a long, long time. And because it was still twilight, that fading, meditative hour, she thought about the world, and all its lakes and streams and rivers and oceans, all the precious water in the world. And then she felt her anger go, felt the waters wash it away, and considered that it was wrong to have judged Julia Meyer so harshly, wrong to judge anyone too harshly. They were all in this thing together. Part of the chorus, chirping, dancing. She glanced at her gentle husband, his eyes ahead where she mightn't see them, fixed on the road, except that she would always see them: green and blue and on fire with his own special vision.

THE PARK
Joan Coldwell

NETTIE watched the proceedings from her usual shady spot under the tall fir. The town crier threw out a few oyez, the mayor gave a speech of thanks, not too sugary, and with a flourish declared the Archibald Newman Memorial Park officially open. The crowd broke into "She's a jolly good fellow" and the slim young councillor struggled forward to present the gift. It was quite the most enormous bottle of Scotch whisky Nettie had ever seen, positively vulgar in fact. There were many in the crowd who thought a floral bouquet would have been more suitable for an old lady, but whisky was what Nettie wanted and whisky was what she got.

She had wanted this land too, all ten acres of it, with its always-changing view of the sea, the humped island and the distant peaks, its rough pathways down to the rocks where at low tide purple starfish cooled their arms in deep crevasses or down to the shell beach where once long ago the first people dug for clams and where as a younger woman she had swum in the dark August nights, making shooting stars of phosphorescence with every stroke.

Now she had given it all away. The Rotary Club could put up benches and tables, families would picnic, children search for seashells, and lovers lie in the mossy hollows. The land and its beauty had been given back for everyone to enjoy. But this much was settled: she could live in her own house, with her flower garden all to herself, until the day she could no longer manage there alone. And that day, Nettie knew, would be the day she died.

Here came a polite young man to ask what Nettie would like from the barbecue: hamburger, hot dog? All Nettie really wanted was to open her big bottle but she asked for just a soft drink, no food. No way would she eat those so-called meats: who knew what scraps of unthinkable body parts went into them. Soon she would go inside the house for a slice or two of smoked salmon on thin brown bread, with capers and onions and lots of pepper.

But first she must be nice. There were the thank-yous and the compliments and then the questions everyone wanted to ask but only a few dared voice, coming right out with them: "How did you get the property in the first place? Inheritance? Sound investment? Lotto win?" Just luck, said Nettie, plain good luck.

The agent, a thin weasel of a man, first came to her door fifteen years ago. Said he was a new neighbour and could he have a chat. Back then her place was much as it was when she bought it thirty years before that, a three-room cabin on half an acre of trees and rock.

"Ever thought of selling? For a double lot this size, with that great view, I could get you 400K. Good money for your children, grandchildren."

"Don't have any."

"Well then, no offence, but a time will come when you'll want an easier place, a condo or a cosy retirement suite. You'll need cash for that big-time — twenty-four hour care and all. I'd try for a half a million. Take down the trees here, the view'd be even better. Could get three houses in here, beauties, yes, maybe seven or eight strata units."

"Over my dead body."

"Silly old cow," thought Archy Newman as he walked away.

Archy was not a man to let rejection put him off. Rejection had been his way of life from the day someone left him on the orphanage steps, a blue baby blanket his only inheritance. He wasn't particularly bright but to survive in the orphanage he'd learned cunning, persuasion, doggedness and a certain superficial charm. These qualities were just right for his chosen profession. Any woman he might have married — and there weren't many of those — turned him down. So he lived alone, frugally, watching his bank account grow and devising plans to keep the tax men at bay.

The only thing Archy wanted to spend money on was a place of his own, a place he could brag about, "just a little spot on the water" to give him prestige in the eyes of his clients. The first house he wanted, a cheap fixer-upper rented to careless tenants, was in fact next door to Nettie Hogg, on a nice fifty-foot lot. He would enjoy cleaning it up and painting, generally putting it to rights; when he'd built a deck and taken down the trees in front he'd have as good a view of the sea as if he sat on a luxury liner. Only when he took in his offer did he learn that Nettie had already struck a deal, pipped him to the post. Within weeks she had knocked down the shack, removed the wire fence and given the plot back to salal, oregon grape and soft green ferns.

By the time Archy first called on Nettie he had finally bought his "little spot". It was quite literally on the water, an old wooden boathouse converted, through who knows what bylaw infractions, into a charming residence just right for one person. Archy was enchanted with it and, to give him his due, furnished it with simple good taste, simple perhaps because he could see no point in spending good money on fancy furniture.

Once settled in the neighbourhood he became obsessed with Nettie and her refusal to sell. At least twice a month he called in on her, carefully avoiding the subject of his real interest. Before he went he made a list of things they might talk about, news items from the paper or bits of gossip picked up on his rounds.

Why Nettie let him in is a puzzle. Was she lonely? Not likely, given the hordes of friends who came by for lavish dinners and could be heard saying their tipsy goodnights clear across the bay. Was she interested in him as a person? It's possible, given she was a writer; they say writers study people and find human nature absorbing. But there must have been a limit to that with Archy. So why did she offer Archy a coffee or a Scotch at least twice a month and sometimes more often? Was she playing a game with him? Cat and mouse? Spider and web? That remained to be seen.

Whatever it was, Archy came and went and was no closer to making a deal. Nettie left for a holiday, to Italy and France and Spain, places Archy could only dream of, and when she returned he asked if there were good sales opportunities there. Instead she spoke of Caravaggio and Vino Nobile di Montepulciano and Monet and omelette aux fines herbes and old Moorish palaces.

Archie went home to his boathouse and thought. On his next visit, he suggested that if Nettie sold up she could buy a vineyard in Tuscany and a converted farmhouse with swimming pool (she had described staying in just such a one) and could sell her own wine and olive oil — the exchange rate was favourable. Nettie threw back her head and laughed.

Some people were not as obstinate as Nettie and this made Archy very busy. He was so busy buying and selling lots, arranging with the fire chief to do practice burns on old houses and clearing trees away with big machines that he had never noticed Nettie taking out her sailboat from its mooring at the marina just across from his windows. So when she invited him for a sail he was both shocked and afraid. Could a woman who must be seventy-five if she was a day sail a boat? He'd never been on one and he didn't like the thought of it but he wouldn't show he was scared.

"I'd like you to see what the land looks like from the water," she said.

And so, since it had been a fabulous business day for Archy, the best he had ever had, he said he would go and what's more they could make it a celebration. "Can we picnic on board?"

"Of course," said Nettie, "it'll be fun."

They met on the dock at five pm. Archy carried a six-pack of Molson's and two bags of chips; Nettie had a hamper loaded with cold chicken, several salads and a bottle of Veuve Clicquot. "It's against the law to drink while sailing, but we'll stay close to shore, and what the heck."

Archy was nervous but he felt better when Nettie got to work on what looked like a pretty serviceable engine and they chugged out of the harbour in fine style. Archy twisted the top off a beer; Nettie declined. Archy had never really looked at her before, but dammit she was a piece of goods right now: short shorts with long brown legs and painted toenails at the bottom of them, some sort of top that showed her bare arms and some perky boobs, a baseball cap and dark specs that made it so he couldn't see her eyes. Surely she couldn't really be in her seventies? Archy cracked open another beer.

The boat had passed his little house (Nettie had never been invited there but she'd peeked through the windows when she knew Archy was out) and was now slowly cruising parallel to the shore across from it. It did Archy's heart good to see the smart new houses on lots he himself had sold over the years; shoulder to shoulder they stood, with their big plate-glass windows, their hot tubs and barbecues, their jetties with massive motor yachts tied up.

"It's overcrowded," said Nettie. "We have to stop putting monster houses on tiny lots — the pollution is appalling, we're killing the trees and the wildlife."

"It's zoned for fifty-foot lots," said Archy. "It's legal."

"And guess what?" He fumbled in a pocket and drew out a cheque. "Sold a property today, that big commercial block in town, and can you believe it, the guy signed the cheque for five million dollars and didn't even write in my company's name. Anybody could write their own name in. All the same it's a steal at that price."

"Better put it away safely," said Nettie. "The wind's coming up."

By now Nettie had cut the engines and hoisted the sails; they were moving along at a fair clip. Archy was into his sixth beer; Nettie hadn't yet opened the hamper.

They were about to round the one undeveloped headland, where towering old-growth trees almost hid the single low rambling house on its six acres. Between this and Nettie's house there were now only four or five ticky-tacky houses along the roadside, all in poor repair and about ready to fall down. Archy knew he would get those for a song but he had no hope of the headland. He still eyed it longingly but he'd given up even trying to get the stubborn old fart to sell; wait till he died and then Archy would tackle the heirs. But Nettie gave thanks daily for that one person who loved the land as much as she did; she knew too that if only she had the money, the old boy would eventually sell to her.

"I need you to crew: go up onto the foredeck and help lower the jib." Archy was terrified but she'd told him right at the beginning that he'd have to follow captain's orders and he daren't back out now.

"Hold onto the mast and when I say haul away, just pull down on the jib."

Archy couldn't tell whether it was the waves or the wind or the beer that made him so wobbly but he did his best. To his amazement he managed to follow orders and down came the jib. It was as he struggled back quite proudly to where Nettie sat at the helm that something struck him hard on the head and he was felled.

Who knows whether Nettie deliberately caused the boom to jibe or whether it was truly an accident? Certainly nobody but Nettie knows that, before she tied an old rusty anchor around Archy's lifeless neck and rolled him overboard, she carefully removed the cheque and put it in her own pocket. And nobody but Nettie knows that her trip to Switzerland the next day was not for vacation purposes but to deposit a five-million dollar cheque in her newly-opened account.

And so it was that bit by bit Nettie followed Archy's example. She gradually bought all the ticky-tacky houses and the properties up to and including his boathouse, until she had ten acres ablaze with natural beauty, no buildings on them except her own, The Boathouse Café and the house on the headland soon to be a museum. And that's how it was that the new park came to be named for a dearly loved friend and neighbour whose body was never found.

ALONE ON THE PENINSULA
Barbara Powell

SHE was old now, even she had to admit it, after years of denial. Nevertheless, she was independent and able to keep the house and property going, with just a little help to do the heavy jobs.

Every day she planned what she would do in the house, she liked to keep it immaculate, tidying, dusting, polishing the furniture and shining the silverware. Everything had to be just right. This was important to her as, although she seldom, if ever, had visitors she wanted to be prepared for them.

The house had once been full of visitors, friends and relatives from the US and the British Isles, when she and her husband had entertained them and taken them out among the Gulf Islands in their cruiser, such a special treat for them, in all the beauty of the sea and mountains. Sometimes they spotted whales on their migration, or dolphins playing in front of the prow as they cruised along, and saw seals basking on the rocks, looking uncomfortably opisthotonic. They could occasionally see a bald eagle swoop down and catch a salmon, almost too big to carry to shore and drag up the rocks. They would fish for salmon themselves and cook one for supper in some quiet cove off one of the islands.

Nowadays she just fantasized about having a visit from some relative or old friend from overseas, or from some casual acquaintance who might drop in to see her and have a cup of tea.

To this end she worked at keeping up her state of preparedness, and every Friday she baked scones and cake to have some home-made fare ready for such an eventuality. When no one came she enjoyed some of this on Sunday evening and put the remainder in the freezer, where it would be available for a weekday guest or to enjoy herself.

She was alone, but not lonely, especially as she had the dog.

She loved her home and each morning would enjoy her breakfast in the sunroom which looked out onto a clearing in the forest of fir and cedar which surrounded the house. As a British visitor had said to her years ago, "Oh, you have your own forest glade!" and, indeed, she did. She fed the squirrels who competed with the bright blue stellar jays for the peanuts, which she put out for them every morning. Chickadees, nut hatches and greedy red-capped finches came to eat the sunflower seeds and suet from the hanging feeders. Tricoloured, red-eyed towhees shyly ventured from the surrounding ivy to feed on seeds on the ground. They all rewarded her in the early summer by bringing their chicks to feed as well. She watched for the quail to come down the path from the stable, the mother leading a string of little ones, followed by the male who would take up his position on an ivy-covered log pile and stand guard as his brood fed or sometimes just settled down to rest in the shade. The self-sufficient robins came for long baths; they had built a high-rise nest complex in the angle of a drain-spout by adding a new nest every year — and it now looked in danger of collapsing. Hummingbirds and butterflies added motion and colour to this magic place.

She enjoyed those wonderful "blue days" as she called them, when she could look out from the window towards the ocean. Sea, sky, and distant islands all looked blue, and towering above them Mount Baker, white and dazzling in the sun, until the sunset cast a pink glow on the snowcapped summit and the range of mountains to the south.

Even in winter there were not many days too cold or wet

enough to prevent her from walking with the dog. Some days there would be a storm with high surf, and crashing waves and she always found excitement in watching them tumbling logs about and tossing them on to the beach. The next day the beach would be covered with seaweeds of so many varieties and colours.

In the spring and summer the fields behind the beach were bright with wild flowers. In May the broom was ablaze with gold, and in June the wild roses came out, a mass of pink, and the air was filled with their scent, then wild lupins would follow, and other flowering shrubs and plants: yellow, purple, blue and white. It was a wonderland!

In the fields and paths she could see the red-winged blackbirds, whose shrill whistles were the first sounds of spring. In the nesting season the male with his bright red-and-yellow epaulettes, perched high in the bushes, kept watch for marauding crows, at the sight of which he would rise with a flash of colour and, joined by other sentinel males, give chase.

She had discovered the ruins of an old house, covered now with periwinkles, where an apple tree still bore fruit, and daffodils and narcissi bloomed each spring, and a little bird house still provided a nesting place for tree swallows. Sad she felt, but nature was surviving and those who walked that way still found pleasure there.

On the beach the driftwood lay bleached like old bones, and the children and young people would build driftwood houses, some large with several rooms. The logs always provided a place to sit and just look at the seascape and watch the birds.

Sometimes there was not a bird in sight, then suddenly they would surface, and float serenely until they spotted another meal swimming underneath. She thought how peaceful they seemed, relaxed and secure, sometimes even asleep, head under wing, in contrast to the constantly alert and ever-fearful songbirds. She saw mandarin ducks, looking magnificently hand painted, loons, bufflehead and redbreasted and hooded mergansers, and homely scoters. The great blue herons stood in shallows, still and motionless. She was always amused to see them, in the evenings, looking so out of place, perched high in the cedar trees. Sometimes she watched playful otters swimming offshore or running across the beach. She dreamed of sharing all this with her relatives from overseas.

She and the dog met other dog-walkers too and they exchanged pleasantries, or chatted as they walked and the dogs played, wrestling or chasing each other, or investigating interesting smells, which she thought of as their way of reading the daily news, to find out who or what had passed that way. When they reached the sea, they went for a cooling swim and fetched sticks. Some even liked to fish, walking belly-deep in the water, eyes intently focused on the bottom, looking for some small prey. What a marvellous time they all had.

Seldom a day passed when she did not meet someone who, like herself, marvelled at the good fortune which had led them to live in such an idyllic place, not only beautiful, but far from the troubles of the world.

When she returned home she would often write down some incident that had pleased her, so that perhaps she could relate it to her family. She was happy and content with the thought of these things which she would talk about with them; it was almost as good as having them there. Perhaps, one day, she would write a book, and, with this fantasy in mind she would often write a little story, just for the pleasure of it.

The friends she knew now were of a younger generation. She resisted inviting them to her home for a meal, not wanting them to feel obligated to accept. Still, she kept everything ready, just in case.

In the evenings there were books and television, the latter to her another marvel. She could just remember the advent of radio with the crystal set and cat's whiskers which had to be "fiddled", resulting in squeals and whines before a voice could be tuned in. Now she could sit comfortably in her living room and enjoy the top performers, even the Olympics — all of this the young could take for granted.

Days and months went by and she kept to her routine, although she only very occasionally had a drop-in visitor, and she realized that it was unlikely that her relatives would ever come. Nonetheless, she kept up the pretence. When they did not come she refused to be disappointed, knowing that their departure would leave a great void in her life, and her fantasies of their visit would be over. She almost preferred to keep the hope alive.

She felt fortunate that life for her was still a pleasure. Her solitude increased her appreciation of her surroundings, and the birds, the dog and her dreams, even if unrealized, gave her motivation, made her life feel purposeful, and she knew that because of this her daily routine must go on, just as it was.

OLAV'S STORY

Margot E Coulter

THEIR story came to me in a dream, I think: the story of Serena and Olav. Or did he whisper it to me as I perched beside his statue on Beacon Avenue in Sidney by the Sea?

It begins as one story, his and hers entwined, but then it separates, as now they sit apart, divided by the street. Outside Tanners Books she sits, reading her book with her purse at her feet: Serena, Olav's old love. She sits there unperturbed, in the fall when red leaves settle on her shoulders, when rain wets her cheeks like the tears she shed long ago. Through all the seasons Serena sits there, unchanged, reading her book.

The fisherman, who seems to lift his head to eternal sunshine, across the street in front of Eyeland Optical, is Olav. Heavy rubber boots stand beside his bare feet, the joy of simple comforts showing on his face. He is contented now but it was not always so.

I wish you had a story to tell, I thought, and began to leave … then stopped, startled by a voice.

"I have, my dear, I have."

Statues don't speak, do they? But there was no one else near.

"No, it's not your imagination. And in the night when the street is empty, I'll prove it to you. Come, if you dare. I'll tell you my story then."

Foolish perhaps, but that night I went back to Sidney, parked the car some distance from the optician's shop, and walked like a thief down the quiet street. When I reached the fisherman's dark figure I stood waiting, actually expecting an offer to sit down. When none came I lowered myself on the bench beside the statue. All remained still, as though the whole town had become a tableau, a setting in some unknown play that had not yet begun. There was only the luminous sky, shedding enough light to define the buildings, the street, and the dark shape beside me.

A soft chuckle made my heart race, then the voice I had heard in the morning spoke to me, clearly, though barely above a whisper:

"So you've come. You're the first to accept my invitation. All the others declined, not even politely, no! They ran." The chuckle again. "Ran!" This time he laughed out loud. The sound echoed back and forth between the buildings. Or was it the wind that had come up suddenly, rattling a loose board before settling again? I looked around. The racket might have wakened the whole town.

"You needn't be afraid. No one hears." Then he continued, sliding smoothly into the narrative of his life, as though he had rehearsed it many times:

I first laid eyes on her, Serena of course, in my old boathouse, down by Bazan Bay. I was standing in the open end contemplating the hulk of a rowboat I'd been in the process of building for two years.

"Looks kind of sad right now, doesn't it?" a voice said behind me. "Could be nice, though, finished."

"Yeah," I answered absent-mindedly, still looking at the boat, wondering what the next step should be and how I would tackle it. "What to do next is the big question."

Then it jumped into my mind: who was I talking to? Embarrassed, I turned around and saw a girl about my own height and so angular she could have been a boy. She wasn't what you'd call *pretty*, except for her eyes: so large they reminded me of tidal pools in sand, and, as tidal pools reflect the mood of the sky, so the colour of her eyes reflected hers, changing from grey to green to blue. I didn't find that out until much later, you understand, as I did other things that often made me forget that she was only a girl. Just like me, she was restless, forever searching, wanting to know, rarely still. But unlike me she was happy with herself, and that was the only part of her that suited her name: Serena.

We stood staring at each other, until she laughed. No giggle, no girlish titter, no. A snorting, loud, infectious laugh that brought us both to tears. When we finally stopped, our crazy grins still pasted on our faces, she introduced herself. "My name's Serena. My father says my mother was inspired by an imp to call me that, and then the imp took possession of me, just to fool people." She held out her hand. "What's yours?" I liked her handshake, it was firm like a boy's.

"Olav Olavson," I answered, in as manly a tone as my fourteen years could muster.

"Olav Olavson," she sang, giving my name a rhythm with a strong O and a quick-soft *lav*, a strong O again and a quick-soft *lavson*. "I like that. It's different."

I grew an inch taller in seconds. "It's Norwegian," I said, "my family came from there."

He fell silent for a long time, so long that I began to fear that we had lost our strange contact. Finally, softer, wistful, his voice came again. "I think I fell in love with her then, only I didn't know it."

Again, that long silence during which I hardly dared breathe for fear of breaking the spell. When he did speak the wistfulness was hidden, as it is often hidden under the voices of old people who remember:

"How'd you get the boat this far?" Serena asked.

"My uncle helped me," I told her, although in truth it was I who helped him. Two years before, when I'd just recovered from a bad case of chicken pox that left me uninterested in anything, my uncle, who was a boat builder, had come to the rescue by suggesting that we build a boat together — "the nicest little rowboat for two", as he put it. And it had done the trick. For two summers we planned, got the wood together, sawed and sanded, hammered and glued in that old shed. But that was then. My uncle married and moved to the other side of Canada. Now I was on my own ...

As though she could read my mind Serena said, "Would you let me help? I'm good at making things."

I looked at her doubtfully. "A girl," I said, "and tools? Hammering, sawing?" I shook my head. "Na, it wouldn't work."

She looked dejected, scuffing the dust on the floor with her foot. Half turning away she said, "You could try me, you know. It wouldn't cost you anything, and it might be fun."

I didn't say yes right away although I wanted to, because by now I, too, thought it might be fun, a chance to show off what I knew about boat building. "Well, okay," I finally agreed, pretending reluctance; then, rather condescendingly, "You could hand me things while I work, tools, materials and ... well, whatever."

So it began, that first summer of building the boat together. Serena would come running along the beach in the morning, often still munching her breakfast. I'd be in the shed already, impatiently tinkering with this or that while waiting for her.

"Morning, Olav!" she'd shout as she ran; then, having arrived at the shed, she'd collapse on the floor and ask breathlessly, "So, what's next?"

Later in the day the shed often became unbearably hot but she didn't seem to notice. Sweat running down her face, her hair stringy with it, she worked with total concentration, and whatever she attempted turned out well and neatly done. We'd long since gotten beyond her "handing me things".

"Where'd you learn all this, knowing what tools to use and how to use them?" I asked her one day.

"I've got three brothers," she said, as though that would explain anything. Then she added, "They all build things. Planes and gliders mostly, and kites."

She'd sit on her haunches, her eyes closed as though meditating, staring inside her head at a problem we'd just discovered; something that didn't fit and we couldn't understand why. When I tried to say something, she fluttered a hand in front of her face as if brushing away a pesky fly. "Don't say anything, don't say anything!" And then, triumphantly, "I've got it, Olav, see?" She pointed to a measurement in the plans that we'd confused with another one.

We didn't complete the boat that summer. Other things interfered from time to time. And suddenly, it seemed, the holidays ended, and Serena returned to her home in Vancouver. On parting, she became unusually formal as she gave me her hand. "Goodbye, Olav Olavson," she said, with a smile that nearly broke my heart. "We'll meet again next year," and added softly, "if God will."

That "if God will" stuck in my mind. It was such an odd thing for her to say. We'd never talked about God. In the end I dismissed it as something Serena would say, and no one would ever know whether she meant anything by it.

As if the moon had risen above the rooftops, the street was suddenly awash with a light that let me see it in greater detail than I had been able to earlier. I hadn't noticed before how few trees were along it, how prominent the telephone poles and the strings of wire between them were. Further down, on the opposite side, was a long low building with a sign that read MITCHELL & ANDERSON. How was it that it seemed so unfamiliar?

"You're seeing the past of Beacon Avenue. The way it used to be when I was young. A busy place. Not so much with tourists as with working people: farmers and cannery workers down by the water, and others who worked in the sawmill. Sure, this was a bustling place. That's what made me almost forget the summer and Serena, except in odd moments, and then it was like someone else's dream."

With this explanation the old street dissolved, and bit by bit resumed its modern look. The lumber store gave way to the Landmark Building, the sidewalks were as I knew them, and Olav picked up the thread of his story:

The coming of next summer brought me back to the boathouse. I had avoided it since Serena left. To continue working on the boat without her seemed too much of a chore. Now I thought I had better make sure that everything was ready for her return. As I pulled away the sheets of plywood that protected the opening, the dusty smell of the little building welcomed me like an old friend, and when the holidays began I went there every morning hoping to see Serena running along the beach, hoping to hear her "Morning, Olav!" Three mornings went by, and then the fourth. On my unhappy way home, her "if God will" came unbidden into my mind. *If.* Perhaps it wasn't willed after all, for her to come back.

The fifth day began as cold and grey as I felt. I sat on the floor beside the boat, morosely stroking the planks of its nearly finished hull when "Morning, Olav!" sounded above the holler of the wind, and, as if touched by a current, my body flung itself up and out onto the beach.

"Morning, Serena!" I shouted back, and, repeating her own favourite phrase, "So, what's next?" And then we stood there laughing. Just laughing.

We finished the boat that summer. Stained it, varnished it slick and shiny, truly a beauty with her clean, elegant lines.

"It needs a name, Olav. We can't go on just calling it *boat*," Serena said.

I'd already thought of that. "I'd like to call her *Serena*," I said, and could feel myself blushing.

"No, oh no, Olav. I'm flattered, but one Serena is quite enough. Just think, what if the imp gets into the boat? Then she'll spring a leak and you'll say *Serena* sprang a leak." At which we half killed ourselves laughing. Then, excited as she used to get when she'd solved a problem, she announced, "I've got it, Olav! We'll call her *Summer* !"

I agreed; it was a good name. With fine brushes and white paint we wrote *Summer* in flowing script on her bow and stern. A wavy line flowed from under the S to just past the R.

We launched her the next morning and christened her in a solemn ceremony in which we both had words to say:

I: "In summer you were born,"
Serena: "In summer you grew up,"
I: "In the name of all that is holy,"
Serena: "Under the sea,"
I: "And above the sea,"
Together: "We christen you *Summer* ..."

Then we emptied a bottle of ginger ale over her bow, not daring to smash it against her shiny new hull. We pushed her into the water and went for our first voyage all along Bazan Bay, both of us rowing, and singing not very musically at the top of our voices: *Row, boys, ro-ow, to Cali-forni-o, there's plenty of rum where I am from, on the banks of the Sacramento.* We weren't sure or concerned about the words but the rhythm seemed perfect.

This time I was glad when Olav paused. I sensed a change coming to this story of perfect friendship, of unfettered, carefree times, and I didn't want it to end. He seemed to feel the same, for the pause was long. Finally, with a sigh, he went on:

Summer didn't spring a leak, not that first year anyway. We spent all our time on her, washing and scrubbing and otherwise fussing when we couldn't go out on the water. When the holidays ended,

Serena said her formal goodbye. "We'll meet again next year, if God will."

The summer remained fresh in my mind throughout the year, even though I would not admit to myself how much I missed Serena. As often as I could I took *Summer* out on the water. In defiance of my loneliness I sang, *Row, boys, ro-ow, to Cali-forni-o, there's plenty of rum where I am from, on the banks of the Sacramento*. But it was all bravado, and anyway, my voice broke and I could only shout.

Finally the long-awaited summer returned and with it the holidays and Serena. I did as I had the year before, waited for her in the boathouse, and on the fifth morning was rewarded with hearing her shout from afar, "Morning Olav!", again and again until the last breathless "Morning Olav" sounded from the opening of the shed.

"So what's next?" I responded. And then we stood and stared, noticing the changes in each other. Serena had lost much of her angularity, she'd rounded out in all kinds of places that I would have blushed to name. Her formerly unruly mop of hair had been cut in a straight line from one end of her jawbone to the other with bangs over her forehead so that the dark sheen of it smoothly framed her pixy face. I would no longer be able to think of her as a boy with a girl's name — and, oh yes — she was *pretty*.

She broke the silence. "Your voice, Olav, it sounds ..." She faltered. "It sounds so deep." She stopped then. "And you've grown. My goodness, look at your shoulders!" Suddenly she laughed, that same old snorting laugh of hers. "Just listen to me, I sound like Grandmama."

We got over that first strangeness with each other but try as we would, we could not completely recapture the ease of the past two years. I now found it difficult to ignore her being a girl, and she, I think, found it equally difficult to ignore my being a boy. I sometimes resented the change, felt betrayed by it, betrayed by *her* who couldn't help it any more than I could. Then I would argue with her, my temper rising over the most ridiculous, unimportant things, until Serena, much wiser than I, would turn and walk away.

Other times I was excited by the change. Then I wanted to protect her, and felt slighted when she'd jump into the boat without taking my outstretched hand. I would insist then on rowing *Summer* by myself. Then, when she ignored my insistence, taking up her oars to row, I would pout, and refuse to talk. Yet Serena always found ways to restore the peace, and everything would be all right — for a while.

The holidays ended. We took *Summer* out for a last row even though the weather seemed a little uncertain. *Row, boys, ro-ow* ... Serena began softly with a faraway look, as though she were singing about a memory. She rowed and sang. I watched her and listened, not joining in the song, the boisterous song that had suddenly become sad and lonely. When it ended, she pulled her oars in, and turning a tear-glistening face to me said, "I'm not happy, Olav Olavson. Please let's go back."

I didn't know how to comfort her. I couldn't find the words. I, too, was filled with a nameless sorrow.

The wind struck like a slap. We tried to row into the suddenly rising waves but they played with our puny efforts. The boat was tossed like a toy, then rose so high on a wave that our oars dangled uselessly in empty space. Then it was smashed onto the beach.

Stunned, at first not realizing that we were on land, we found ourselves still in the boat, or what was left of it. Serena and I fared better than she did. Her bow had splintered from the impact with the rocks and stones on the beach. Except for some scratches, Serena looked untouched. She crawled over to where I lay, sprawled against the shattered remains of the bow.

"You're bleeding," she whispered, as though a louder voice would make it worse.

A deep gash seeped blood down my arm. "It's not as bad as it looks," I said. "It doesn't even hurt." And then I put my arms around her shaking shoulders. I could feel her bones, sharp and delicate through her wet clothes, and a great tenderness filled me. We clung to each other in what seemed like a vast timelessness but probably lasted only a few minutes, and then I kissed her hair, her forehead, her cheek, and shyly, her mouth.

"Can you walk, Serena? You're not hurt?" I finally asked.

She seemed strangely quiet — so unlike her — but she answered softly, "I'm not hurt."

Stiffly, I got to my feet, and bending, pulled her gently up. Before she left for Vancouver the next day, she said her usual "Goodbye, Olav Olavson, we'll meet again," and stopped there, not adding the rest.

The pause was short this time, Olav continued almost immediately. "The rest won't take long," he said:

In the fall a letter arrived. My nervous excitement turned to painful disappointment as I read its short message. I read and re-read it so many times I can still recite it from memory, after all these years. "Dearest Olav," it began. "Grandmama died last night. We are leaving for Sidney this afternoon to make funeral arrangements and to take care of her estate. I can't tell you how sad I am — I loved her so much. Will I see you? I don't know." And she signed it, "Yours, Serena."

Serena's grandmother had lived in the same beautiful house on Robert's Point for most of her life and had been well respected, even loved, by many, so it was a large crowd that attended her funeral, and no one seemed to find anything remarkable in my presence. Serena, her little white face startling above her black coat, sat between her two older brothers. I wanted to go to her when the service ended but lost my nerve.

I carried my troubled restlessness to the boathouse the next day. I hadn't been there since I'd deposited the wrecked pieces of *Summer*. Would I ever put her together again? Would Serena be there to do it with me? "Humpty-Dumpty," I said to myself. I didn't believe *Summer* could be resurrected, nor could the past summers be retrieved.

With my back to the opening I didn't become aware of her until she whispered, "Morning, Olav."

I answered just as softly: "So … What's next?"

Then I turned.

She was studying the sorry remnants of *Summer*. "Oh, Olav. Will everything be sad now all the time?"

"No, Serena. We'll be happy again." Brave words, that I couldn't make myself believe.

In the raw November breeze we huddled on a log outside the boathouse, and there, staring out over the grey horizonless water, she told me the rest of the bad news. Her father had accepted a post at a university in Sydney, Australia, the family would be moving there in January. Her grandmother's house, which Serena had inherited, would be closed up, until she was old enough to decide what to do with it.

We sat silently for a long time. I had no words of comfort for either of us. Finally, Serena rose, and together we walked along the edge of the water, stopping now and then, not knowing how to say goodbye.

In the end Serena made it simple. She held out her hand with a tremulous smile and said, "Goodbye, Olav Olavson."

"Will we meet again?" I asked.

"If God will." She nodded quickly, stepping forward to kiss me as gently as I had kissed her in the wreckage of *Summer*. She turned then and walked away, not once looking back. I followed her with my eyes, her figure blurred, swimming in my tears, until she was just a speck on the beach and then nothing. I picked up a flat pebble and flung it over the water. It didn't skip but sank with a dull plop.

You're wondering how I came to be a fisherman. Well, I'm coming to that. I had other dreams — university, a science degree, becoming an oceanographer. None of that happened because my father fell off a ladder and was left with a broken spine, a quadriplegic. There was no insurance — I would have to support my parents as well as myself. It sounds heartless now but I blamed my father for his accident, and in my heart accused him of ruining my life. I couldn't bear to look at him in his wheelchair, couldn't bear my mother's determinedly cheerful face. I wanted to get as far away from them as I could and signed on as a deck hand on a commercial fishing boat that worked along the northern coast. My contract ran for four months, but when the months were over I signed on again. I welcomed the hard work, the primitive, comfortless life; it left no time for dreams, no energy for regrets. Apart from that the money was good, and out of a sense of guilt I sent it all home.

Then my father died, and a month later, my mother followed. I was free! Still, I needed money, and where else could I make it faster than fishing in northern waters? So I stayed on. Months turned into years. I was used to the life now and couldn't imagine myself at a university. Instead, with the money I'd saved I bought my own boat.

In all those years did I think of Serena? Oh, yes. When I thought at all, I thought of her, wondered where she was, what filled her life, wondered if she had ever gone back to Sidney to claim her inheritance on Roberts Point. I had stood in front of it after my mother's funeral, stared at its shuttered windows, the neglected garden, and thought how pretty it had been not so long ago.

Thirty years I stayed away from Sidney, neither happy nor unhappy. Suddenly, in the thirty-first year, a longing to go home overcame me. There was a cottage on Orchard Avenue I'd admired when I was young. As luck would have it, it was still there, standing empty, needing some work, but then, I didn't have much else to do after I sold the boat.

When Olav stopped speaking I let my lips form the question uppermost in my mind: "Serena. Did you never see her again?"

Oh, yes, I did see her. It was a fine morning the summer after I returned. Sitting on a log near the place where the boathouse used to be. She was sitting there quietly, staring out to sea. Of course, I didn't know immediately that it was her — how could I after all that time? Still, there was something familiar, something remembered in her posture, the way she held her head. I asked if I could share her log. Startled at my voice as though awakened from a dream, she turned, and smiled that same shy smile that nearly broke my heart so long ago.

"Serena?" Although I was certain by then. She nodded. "I should shout: Morning, Olav! So what's next?" She chuckled and went on, "Don't look so surprised, Olav Olavson, it was your voice that gave you away." And then she laughed that great snorting laugh of hers and I joined in, as I had that first time we met.

So we sat on that fine summer morning, sometimes talking about the years we'd spent apart, sometimes remembering the times we'd been together, sometimes in comfortable silence. At parting she asked, "The boat, your fishing boat that you sold, what did you name it?"

"*Summer II*, I called it.' I smiled. '*Summer II*.'

She smiled too, and stretched out both her hands, taking mine in hers. "Goodbye, Olav Olavson. We'll meet again, perhaps."

I waited for him to continue but the silence stretched into minutes. He did not react to any of the questions forming in my mind. I realized then that his story had ended, that he was content, that Olav would add nothing more.

And so they sit, the two lovers, Serena and Olav. Apart, but not too far.

PICKLED EGGS
Anny Scoones

I once ate a pickled egg at a village pub in England, and after I'd moved to Glamorgan Farm and started raising chickens, I decided to make pickled eggs here on my farm. To myself I boasted that my eggs would be especially wonderful, as I intended to use fresh eggs laid by my heritage and hardy hens — all different shapes and sizes and varieties.

I telephoned Dad and got my old Polish grandmother's recipe for pickling brine, a potent Slavic mixture of vinegar, dill, mustard and spices. I sterilized the big mason jars with boiling water. The eggs were first hard-boiled and pierced with a toothpick before they sat in the brine to be pickled.

The jars of eggs sat on my kitchen shelf in amongst Mum's apple jellies, some bottled salmon, and little wooden boxes of dried herbs. After three week the pickling was complete. The eggs were delicious. I ate them on a cool spring evening by the fire.

That autumn, I decided to enter a jar of pickled eggs in the Saanich Fair. I repeated the procedure carefully. The theme of the fair was "the olden days", so I found an antique jar, the kind with a glass lid. Mum had done a funny watercolour of my Naked Neck rooster, so I used that on the label. Part of the Fair's expectation is that entrants educate the public, so I wrote a little about the Naked Neck hen, and the other heritage poultry hens who had laid the eggs I used.

The eggs sat patiently on my shelf for two weeks until the big day arrived. The night before the fair, everyone takes their displays and entries to the various tents. Everyone vies for the best space and the best light for display. It can be quite competitive. Women with huge colourful dahlias shove each other out of the way and it is just downright volatile in the home baking section.

I carried my pickled eggs to the small wooden display area and put the jar down carefully. There were rows of relishes, burgundy-coloured preserves, pink herbal vinegars, and interesting-looking bottles of pickled beets and mushrooms, all tied with silk ribbons, raffia, or elegant twine. The honey in the corner, in gleaming, resin shades of ambers and ochres, was labelled with exotic names like "Golden Rod and Sweet Pea," "Fireweed" and "Saanich Wild Flower".

There was only one other jar of pickled eggs, but it gave me a sinking feeling — it looked so perfect. First of all, the brine was crystal clear, and three gleaming white eggs sat in perfect balance with two sharply-cut slivers of red pepper arranged against the side of the jar. My misshapen Naked Neck eggs were plopped into a brown and cloudy brine, absent of any decoration. But taste was part of the judging, and I surely would make up the ground there — I trusted Dad's Polish brine recipe.

His mother had pickled everything — that was how food was preserved in the Eastern European countries. When I had visited Belarus a few years earlier, my entire lunch was pickled — pickled cabbage, pickled tomatoes, beets and fish, and pickles too of course. If you can get your hands on a traditional Slavic pickling recipe, you cannot go wrong. That is why I was going to win the pickled egg competition.

I had also made a label describing the three breeds of hens that my eggs came from:

"The little egg was laid by the miniature *Silky*, a small hen with extremely fluffy feathers resembling goose down. The largest egg came from the rare *Hungarian Naked Neck*, originally thought to be a cross with a wild turkey, thus having no feathers on its neck. The middle-sized egg was laid by the *South American Araucana* hen, whose shell is blue or green."

So I had an interesting label propped up behind my jar, three unique eggs, and a delicious traditional brine — I could not lose!

They judge on the first morning of the fair, award the ribbons, and sometimes write little comments on the entries. In the afternoon everything is on display for the public to see. Entrants are asked not to remove their displays until the fair closes three days later.

I love the Saanich Fair and all the activity. One year Mum was here visiting, and we went to the fair on the morning of the last day. It was raining and we watched the pig obedience class from the soaking green bleachers with the rain pouring off our hoods. Three teenagers were trying to control their very naughty pigs in the mud. One pig was terribly interested in another pig and paid no attention whatsoever to his exasperated owner. But the judge, a nice blond woman in a dark-green poncho with a clipboard under her arm, gave each of the handlers a little wet blue ribbon. She explained to the spectators (Mum and me) that even though the boy had had trouble controlling his pig, his knowledge of swine ailments was far beyond what was expected from an exhibitor.

After the pigs, I had a caramel apple. They always look so good standing in a grand line under the glass counter, but they are so disappointing in a way, and extremely awkward to eat on their little sticks. Mum and I stood under the eaves of the draught-horse barn, out of the rain. I took one hopeless bite and then my apple fell off its stick into the wet gravel and rolled away down the hill.

The sky was a thick, low grey. Mum and I had just decided to go home and sit by the fire when we heard a great commotion coming from around the corner of the barn. Before we could assess the situation, a miniature horse pulling a two-wheeled cart, in which sat a huge woman in a billowing dress of light blue chiffon, came streaking around the corner and almost ran us down. The woman was screaming, "Whoa, you son of a bitch! Goddamn you! *Whoa!!*" She had both her handbrakes on and they left great deep troughs in the gravel. The disobedient little horse galloped past us towards the outdoor café, where thankfully nobody was sitting. The cart caught the corner of a green umbrella and pulled over the whole table. The top of the umbrella caught the awning above, ripping it from the building. The little horse just kept galloping, now from fright rather than disobedience. Deck chairs went flying in all directions. The frightened horse raced on, dragging the broken cart, bits of harness, a chair, and umbrella and the ripped awning behind him. The woman tried to scramble off the back but her blue dress had become tangled in the wheel.

Finally she tumbled off the cart and rolled onto the soggy grass, her dress torn off at the thigh. Her little horse charged away toward the rides and the cotton-candy booths.

A man in navy-blue overalls ran to help the woman. She was terribly humiliated but okay. I heard her say to him, "That little bastard! This is the last time he'll come to the Saanich Fair."

But this year my pickled eggs were being judged. I walked nonchalantly past the beautiful shelves of winning preserves covered in red, blue and purple rosettes. As I got closer I could see that the blue ribbon was on the jar with the clear brine, not mine. Not only that, I hadn't even received second place! To make matters worse, the judges had scrawled on my little entry tag, "Not sealed properly and LEAKS."

There was no way I was going to let my pickled eggs sit there for three more days with that mean little note attached.

But how could I get them past the old men sitting at the door guarding the place? Maybe I should say that I was going out of town and would not be there to pick my eggs up in three days. Maybe I should just carry them out brazenly as if I was unaware of the three day rule. I thought of slipping the entry tag into my hand and not picking up my eggs at all — ever. At least if the tag was gone, thousands of people would not see me accused of trying to give the pickled-egg judges botulism.

God — I just didn't know what to do, and I was becoming very tense the more I witnessed the lines of people strolling past the shelves and reading each tag! "Do these people not have a life!?" I remember thinking, "Are they that bored that they have to read every single damn tag? I mean, there are two billion other things to see at the fair for God's sakes — why are they all so determined to stare at the pickled eggs?!"

Finally I could not bear it another minute. I marched up to the shelf, picked up my unsealed jar of eggs and the label and walked, as if I meant business, across the beige room, under the fluorescent light, toward the door. I could see the real world outside — the shiny red tilt-a-whirl chairs spinning with screaming children, the candy-apple stand, the clown in the dunk tank, all under a big, warm, blue sky.

The old men got up from their chrome chairs and took their positions by the doors. My heart sank.

"Nothing leaves this room until Monday," a stooped man with loose dentures in a diamond-patterned cardigan said. His friend in suspenders stood behind him. I could see people eating hot dogs out on the lawn, and a man on a flatbed truck weighing the biggest pumpkins I have ever seen.

"I have permission," I lied. "A lady upstairs at the desk said it was okay because I'll be out of town on Monday."

"Would that have been Hilda or Nettie?" the suspendered man feebly asked the other.

"Best I go up and check," said the one in the diamond cardigan. He shuffled off toward the stairs as his friend continued to stand by the door

"I'll wait out there in the sun," I said. Then I walked out and headed straight for the parking lot. I started running as soon as I rounded the corner. With brine splashing onto my shirt, I ran through the dairy barn. The huge shiny black cows, with their clean pink udders and mouths full of green alfalfa turned their heads slowly in vague curiosity. I took a short cut through the home-crafts building, scooted through the restored antique farm-equipment display and ran out the gate toward the field where my car was parked. I had escaped!

When I arrived home, I changed my shirt and sat out on the deck. I felt like eating a pickled egg, but the judges had given me serious doubts. Because the jar had not been sealed, was I in danger of being poisoned?

I sat and looked at the jar on the little round glass table. It would be such a waste of three good eggs not to eat them. I sat for a long time. Then I did a few chores. That way, if I died, at least all the animals would be fed and clean for the night.

The eggs were delicious. I ate all three and waited. Nothing happened.

SONG CYCLE

Anthony Taylor

CURIOUS that we call our planet Earth when seven-tenths of its surface is water. Yet billions of years ago, when the planet was in its infancy, rocks were more evident. Flung from the earth's hot crust, spilling from long craggy fissures, they cracked and whirled as they cooled. Then, in a series of slow, titanic fluctuations, water began to prevail. The steam from the solidifying magma rose into the atmosphere, condensed there and fell onto the rock, etching it, shaping it, changing its chemistry. And so, over time, the water transformed the rock.

Rock, water. Loving antagonists, resisting each other's embrace. Rock, the fire; water, the seducer; each in the end succumbing to the other. A process silent in our memories yet full of miraculous sound. Water dripping, babbling, rushing, splashing. Rolling rocks: scrabbling, crashing. Together they played a kind of Wagnerian symphony and this peninsula was part of it, our saltwater song.

As well as spewing forth igneous matter, the fires burning just beneath the surface contorted its shape, pushing up peaks, tearing them apart to form deep chasms, and then the water began its real work. The mountains were worn away by rivulets and streams and mighty rivers coursing through the valleys until only flatlands were left (and even these are being eroded although this is taking more time). And the sediments from all this ceaseless action – boulders, rocks, pebbles, scree, soil, sand – were dumped by the rivers into the sea.

These vast amounts of matter, the rubble of a continent, did not get carried far. Huge troughs, known as geosynclines, deeper than the highest mountains, were formed by the earth's oceanic crust continually sinking to accommodate the falling sediment, all along the edge of the land. Periodically the troughs filled, and the giant mass was forced upward again, and a new, super-high range of mountains was created. Then granite from the upper crust was thrust into the sedimentary folds, and occasionally broke through, forming highly explosive, acid volcanoes, altogether different from the gentler, quiet kind rising underwater in the oceans. Our region is unique because we have not only one, but two mountain ranges at the continent's western edge — the older, quieter Rocky Mountains, and the younger, higher, more bumptious Coastal Range. This particular formation is found nowhere else in the world.

The mountain ranges were sculpted still further by melting glaciers. Rivers dug out more valleys. Islands popped up, and vanished; though some remained, hovering near the landmass. The waves hurled against them, or licked at their edges, leaving more sediment: boulders, pebbles, sand, clay. All of which, though sedimentary, were the by-products of the original igneous material; that is, all are, essentially, granite.

Granite, the hard crystalline stone glittering with flashes of quartz, is the basic land-building material, the stuff from which continents and their breakaway islands were, and continue to be, made. All other rocks, with the exception of the carbon-based limestones, are derived from humble, hard, Herculean granite. Small islands can exist without it but, geologically speaking, they don't last long. The flat coral atolls found dotted through the Pacific are basically unstable and are, in geological terms, sinking swiftly into the sea.

The islands here, including this peninsula, are the debris of the long, tumultuous union of water and granite. They are bits of what is still today the earth's largest single granite mass. Stretching from Alaska to Mexico, it was first described many years ago by Reginald Aldworth Daly, a Canadian geologist who has never been given his due. He named it the Coast Range Batholith — *batholith* from the Greek *bathus*, for deep, to describe the rocks formed deep within the earth's crust. Granite is thus a pristine substance, because water hasn't had a chance to wear it down completely, or alkalize its chemical composition. It is still in the process of becoming.

Our local granite, like all granites, is composed of three, basic, rock-forming minerals. One, the simple compound of silicon and oxygen, is quartz. The second, more common, is felspar: a complex substance rich in silicon and oxygen, but also containing alkalis such as sodium and calcium. Both quartz and felspar are light in colour. The third, darker mineral — always some kind of ferromagnesian substance — appears less frequently in acid rocks such as granite.

Water meets rock, and the land at our feet is born. Rushing water works like a hammer, beating the quartz into sand. The dark minerals are crunched into tiny flakes of clay. But the dominant felspars are broken down by water chemically as well as physically, and are thus transformed. The calcium released is used by living things to form bones and shells. Only after the calcium in the felspar has combined with carbon in a life form does this material get deposited as limestone. But sodium, also present in felspar, is nature's wild card. Much harder to recycle, it gets dumped into the oceans. It's what makes salt water salt.

Because our batholith is so huge, and its rock so acid, the whole of the landmass should be desert and one of the most infertile places on earth. But water has turned the rock into the world's largest biomass, ten times the size of the Amazon rainforest. The forest, through which the inland sea flows, is home to the world's largest trees, and to countless millions of salmon, which are food for the coastal grizzly, the world's largest land-dwelling carnivore.

The secret of the fertility is in this trinity. The fish swim in from the sea, bringing nutriments rich in nitrogen for the trees and smaller plants. And unlike salmon found elsewhere, the salmon here do not return to the sea, but die on spawning in the rivers, sacrificing themselves to supply protein for the bears. The fastidious bears bite out the best chunks of fish and drop the rest in the forest, fertilizing the river-sheltering trees. The acid soil becomes more alkaline, and the trees, which are giant pumps, eject water into the sky. They help make the clouds and thus bring the rain, which in turn succours the land, encouraging a complex sub-fauna, and new generations of fish.

Trees, fish, bears — each part of a lifeline, as dependent on each other as a rope's three twisted strands. Billions of fish, the great bears that feed on them, the giant trees that thrive from them, all ineluctably entwined.

Nobody knows exactly when or where life originated, but we do know how. It almost certainly happened in a myriad of places — it is easy to imagine it happening here. Our peninsula was formed from broken rock, the rocks dissolved and transformed by water, the universal solvent. In swampy places, often at the mouths of rivers, conditions are perfect for the formation of life. To the naturalist this is the most interesting, most fascinating reaction of them all.

Surrounding us everywhere on the surface of this planet, water is rarely found anywhere else in the universe, yet here it is a common substance. Out in space the only really common element is hydrogen, the lightest and simplest. But that is only among the stars. Here on earth it joins with oxygen in a lopsided, curiously asymmetric molecule built of one oxygen to every two hydrogen atoms, exactly twenty-three and a half degrees apart.

Rock and water, water and rock. The more we contemplate them the simpler and more complex they become. All life emerges from their union. On earth hydrogen also combines with other elements to make compounds like ammonia (nitrogen and hydrogen) and methane (carbon and hydrogen). Found in swampy places, these compounds react with water to form the more complex deoxyribonucleic acid — DNA, the basic chemical of life.

Without water, then, this one, lopsided molecule, breaking in its peculiar asymmetry all the established rules of nature, life could never have occurred. Our trees and bears, our fields of daffodils and pumpkins, the hens that peck at the ground, laying the eggs we eat in our cafés for breakfast — might never have been.

It's odd, I know, but I like to meditate on these things. Chemical equations and geologic formations are never boring to me. I like standing on the foreshore, gazing off to sea, imagining the climactic shifts and parries of the continental shelf below, wondering what dramatic tectonic havoc our planet will surprise us with next. What new landscapes will emerge, what valleys, what rivers; what deltas and flood plains. My ears are tuned to a different kind of music: rock-crunching symphonies, bubbling concertos, saltwater songs. Canute-like, I see the earth boil, titanic waves soar and curl and part, exposing the underwater peaks, slowly being sculpted themselves into ever more fantastic shapes: needle-like spires and smooth-surfaced mesas rising from the silt on the ocean's floor. It's not as if I forget the condos and marinas and shopping malls, or the houses hung like aeries on far wooded cliffs, or the numberless variety of seacraft bobbing on their moorings; gliding, whizzing or lumbering through the waves. It's as though I've corrected my vision somehow, refocused a lens, and what I see is so large and wild and wonderful, and at the same time so miraculously microscopic, that all my puny strivings here on the peninsula are briefly laid to rest.

CONTRIBUTORS
(in order of appearance)

Philip Kevin Paul's poems have been published in *Breathing Fire: Canada's New Poets, An Anthology of Canadian Native Literature* and *BC Studies*. The son of the late Chief Philip Paul — the co-founder of the Union of BC Indian Chiefs and National Native Brotherhood — Kevin lives in his W̱SÁNEĆ homeland of Brentwood Bay. He is also an amateur lightweight boxer; before a hand injury, he was ranked fifth in BC and thirteenth in Canada. He has worked as an instructor at the Saanich Adult Education Centre. His book *Taking the Names down from the Hill* was published in 2003.

Rick Hudson was born in South Africa and grew up on a farm in the eastern Cape. He received a BSc Engineering from Cape Town University, and a PhD from Cambridge University in England, where he married Rhodesian-born Phillipa Gardiner. A keen mountaineer, he led or was a member of numerous climbing expeditions to Patagonia, Greenland, East Africa and the Himalayas. Moving to Canada, the family settled on Vancouver Island in 1981. He is the author of three books, and writes for a variety of magazines, newspapers and journals, on science and outdoor adventure topics.

Margaret Thompson was born and educated in England and came to Canada in 1967. She worked as a high school and college teacher of English for many years, retiring in 1996. She writes non-fiction and fiction, and is the author of four books, including the young adult novel, *Eyewitness*, which received a BC2000 Book Award. Her prizewinning essays, stories and poems have also appeared in *Event, Grain, Prairie Fire* and *The Amethyst Review*. A long-time resident of Fort St James, she has now exchanged six-month winters for year-round gardens on the Saanich Peninsula. She is also President of the Federation of BC Writers.

Michael Coney is the author of sixteen science fiction novels; some have appeared in as many as seven languages. He has written sixty short stories published in Canada, the US and England, and translated into several languages, including a series set on Vancouver Island. He has also written two humorous novels set in the Gulf Islands: *A Tomcat Called Sabrina* and *No Place for a Sealion*, and a history of the wooden boats once operated by the BC Forest Service, titled *Forest Ranger, Ahoy!* all published by Porthole Press. Mike lives in North Saanich with his wife Daphne. His son Kevin is part-owner of Island Marble Ltd, and his daughter Sally is assistant to the principal of St Margaret's School.

Lorna Crozier has lived on the Saanich Peninsula with poet Patrick Lane for over twelve years. All kinds of good things have happened here, including her receiving the Governor-General's Award for poetry in 1992. The garden she shares with Patrick is a paradise for cats, fish, herons that eat the fish, and raccoons. When she isn't hanging around the peninsula, she's teaching at the University of Victoria in the Department of Writing or on the road with books of poems. Her eleventh book of poetry, *The Apocrypha of Light*, was published by McClelland and Stewart in 2002. She has also written and published essays, most recently in the magazines *Geist* and *Border Crossings*. With Patrick Lane she co-edited *Addicted: Notes from the Belly of the Beast*, and she is the editor of *Desire*, a collection of essays by seven Canadian women.

Sylvia Olsen has lived and worked on the Saanich Peninsula for most of her life. Thirty-one years ago she married into the Tsartlip First Nation where she has raised her four children. Sylvia works in First Nations community development and specializes in housing and community research. She is a new writer and often finds herself writing about the in-between place where First Nations and non-First Nations come together. At this time Sylvia is concentrating her energies on writing fiction for young people.

MAC Farrant is the award-winning author of seven collections of satirical and humorous short fiction, most recently, *Darwin Alone In The Universe* (Talon, May 2003). A novel-length memoir, *My Turquoise Years*, is forthcoming from Greystone Books in 2004. Her work has been dramatized for television and appears frequently on CBC Radio, and in *Adbusters* and *Geist* magazines. Her many anthology contributions include "And Other Stories" (Ed, George Bowering, Talonbooks, 2001) and a commissioned piece on the work of Leon Rooke, Branko Gorjup, Editor (Exile Editions, 2003). She is the west coast organizer and host of the annual Canadian small press ReLit Awards and lives near Sidney, BC.

Pauline Holdstock has published novels, poetry, short fiction and essays in Canada, the UK and Germany. She has won the Federation of BC Writers Award and the Matrix/Random House Prize for fiction, as well as the *Prairie Fire* Personal Journalism Prize. Her new novel, *Beyond Measure*, is published by Cormorant.

Michael Elcock was Athletic Director at the University of Victoria for nearly ten years (and, among other things, gave us UVic's widely-used network of jogging trails). After that he became Tourism Victoria's first CEO. In 1990 he moved with his wife and daughter to Andalusia to work on developing Spain's Expo 92. He has lived in a number of different countries and did his postgraduate studies in Quebec, Sweden, Germany, Belgium and Scotland. He is currently teaching in the International MBA program at Malaspina University-College, and has a non-fiction book coming out next spring, on travel and conflict.

Michael Cullen is a winner of the duMaurier National Playwrighting Competition, the Praxis National Screenwriting Competition and, last year, was a finalist for the Jim Burt Screenwriting Award. He is also the recipient of the Norma Epstein Writing Award from the University of Toronto.

Kathy Page was born in London and recently moved to BC. A novelist and widely anthologized short story writer, she has also written for television and radio. She has taught fiction writing in universities in England, Finland, and Estonia. Her novels include *The Unborn Dreams of Clara Riley*, *Frankie Styne and the Silver Man* and the recently published *The Story of my Face*, which was nominated for the Orange Prize in 2002.

Stephen Hume is columnist and senior writer at the *Vancouver Sun* and teaches creative writing at the University of Victoria. He is the author of half a dozen award-winning books of poetry, essays and natural history, the most recent of which is *Off the Map* which was short-listed for the Hubert Evans Prize. He lives in North Saanich.

Susan Musgrave, born in Santa Cruz, California, was raised on Vancouver Island and published her first book of poetry when she was sixteen. Since then she has written numerous books of poetry and three novels: *The Charcoal Burners*, *The Dancing Chicken* and *Cargo of Orchids*. Her work has been nominated and won awards for fiction and non-fiction as well as poetry, and has been widely anthologized, both in Canada and the US. She lives in North Saanich with her two daughters.

Charlotte Biscay was born in New Orleans. After the death of her musician father she moved with her mother and brothers to Paris, where she later studied Russian history and literature at the Sorbonne's L'Ecole Normale Supérieure. Graduating with honors she then enrolled in a cinematography course and began making documentaries for Ciné-Actualité, eventually becoming one of the first women to make a mark in that organisation. After recording the tumultous events of 1968 with her camera she opted for a quieter life and emigrated to Canada, settling on the Saanich Peninsula with her photographer husband in the 1980s. Ms Biscay, now widowed, is the mother of three grown children: Porthos, Athos and Aramis.

Joan Coldwell was born in Yorkshire but since 1968 has made her home in Deep Cove, where she enjoys gardening, walking, sailing and swimming. Two of her chief passions — books and food — are reflected in her work as a weekly newspaper columnist and freelance radio producer. In another life as university professor she writes extensively on academic themes. She takes an active interest in local politics and currently serves as Vice-Chair of the North Saanich Parks Commission.

Barbara Powell was born in Belfast, Northern Island and after studying at the London Guildhall School of Music and Drama, began a course in veterinary medicine in Dublin, Ireland, graduated and became a member of the Royal College of Veterinary Surgeons. She married another veterinarian and immigrated to Canada, where she worked in virus research for the federal government in Hull, Quebec and at the University of British Columbia before entering private practice in Vancouver and later on the Saanich Peninsula. She travelled extensively with husband Bill, an accomplished polo player, when he played around the world in England, the US, Australia, New Zealand, the West Indies, Argentina and India; and helped him re-establish polo on Vancouver Island. Her hobbies include riding, polo, tennis and writing.

Margot E Coulter, retired from teaching, has settled with her husband in Saanichton where she continues to pursue her interests in painting and writing. She enjoys times spent with family, gardening, listening to classical music, and long walks. Her greatest satisfaction stems from finally having the freedom to set her own goals and the time to fulfill them.

Anny Scoones is an elected councillor for North Saanich. A few of her special interests on council include heritage conservation, parks, bicycle paths, youth projects and the newly formed Community Spirit Committee, which recently held North Saanich's first ever country fair on her historic Glamorgan Farm. She has never published anything except an article in a local gardening magazine about the time her giant purple cabbages were eliminated from the Saanich Fair. She loves her farm which was built in 1871 and includes eleven barns and structures including the outhouse. Many of the old log barns were built from original Saanich timber. She raises heritage breeds of farm animals including the woolly Russian Bashkir Curly horse which grows wool rather than hair, and the Hungarian Naked Neck chicken which is crossed with a turkey. To keep her mind alive she studies philosophy at the University of Victoria.

Anthony Taylor has lived most of his life outdoors, climbing mountains, fishing rivers, studying wild things, and messing about with boats. Educated at King's College, London where the science of geology began, he climbed with the poet Michael Roberts who encouraged him to write for a more general audience. He worked as a scientific officer at the British Museum, taught geology in the UK and Australia and was science master at a school in Scotland. After migrating to Canada he continued teaching and fell in love with British Columbia, writing an outdoor column called "Out and About with Tarka". Boatbuilding has been a passion and he has sailed the inland waters of the west coast. His articles have been published in Canada, UK and Australia.

Sara Dowse was born in Chicago, and lived in New York and Los Angeles before leaving for Sydney, Australia in her late teens. After ten years in Sydney she moved to Canberra where she worked in publishing and as a journalist and public servant. She has published five novels, including *Sapphires*, which was on the Australian short list for the IMPAC Dublin Prize. Ever since arriving in British Columbia in December 1998 she has been working on a sixth one, set in British Mandate Palestine.

Editor's Notes

Michael Coney's "**The Byrds**" was first published in *Changes:Stories of Metamorphoses*, edited by Ian Watson and Michael Bishop, Ace, New York, 1983.

"**Ghost House**" by Lorna Crozier was first published in the summer 1997 edition of *Western Living* magazine. My thanks to Matt O'Grady, the magazine's assistant editor, who was able to recover it from the files.

"**Skidney**" by MAC Farrant first appeared in the May 1999 issue of *Monday* magazine and was subsequently published in the author's *Girls Around the House*, Polestar, 1999.

"**The Turn of the Year**" by Pauline Holdstock is from the author's *Swimming from the Flames*, Turnstone Press, Winnipeg, 1995.

An earlier version of Stephen Hume's essay "**A Saanich Thanksgiving**" first appeared in the *Vancouver Sun*, just before the turn of the millennium.

"**The Gift**" by Susan Musgrave appears in the author's collection of published pieces *Great Musgrave*, Prentice-Hall Canada, Inc, Scarborough, 1989.

Philip Kevin Paul's "**Water Drinker**" appears in his poetry collection *Taking the Names down from the Hill*, Nightwood Editions, Roberts Creek, 2003.

The statues in Margot E Coulter's "**Olav's Story**" were sculpted by Nathan Scott. "Olav", in fact, was modelled on the artist's father-in-law, Peter Clarke, "Selena" on the late Jarmila Thouvenelle.